The
Human Interface

WHERE PEOPLE AND
COMPUTERS MEET

The
Human Interface

WHERE PEOPLE AND
COMPUTERS MEET

Richard A. Bolt

Massachusetts Institute of Technology

Lifetime Learning Publications
Belmont, California
A Division of Wadsworth, Inc.

London, Singapore, Sydney, Tokyo, Toronto, Mexico City

Production Editor: Richard Mason

Designer: Rick Chafian

Copy Editor: Don Yoder

Composition: Bi-Comp, Inc.

Printed in the United States of America

1 2 3 4 5 6 7 8 9 10—87 86 85 84

Library of Congress Cataloging in Publication Data
Bolt, Richard A.
    The human interface.
    Bibliography: p.
    Includes index.
    1. Interactive computer systems. I. Title
QA76.9.I58B65   1984   001.64   84-5768
ISBN 0-534-03380-6-Cloth
ISBN 0-534-03387-3-Paper

For Olga, John Dimitri,
and Nicholas James

Contents

List of Illustrations   ix

Foreword   xiii

Preface   xv

1. Where in the World Is the Information?   **1**

Beyond the Keyboard   1
Using Space to Organize Data   3
Space and Computers   5
Highlights   6
Notes   6

2. The Uses of Space   **8**

The Media Room   8
The World of Dataland   9
Other Ways of Using Space   21
Design Issues   26
Future Developments   29
Highlights   29
Notes   30

3. Speech and Gesture   **35**

Machines That Recognize Speech   36
Speech and Context   39
When Gesture Is Gesture   41

Capturing Speech in the Media Room   41
Capturing Gesture in the Media Room   43
"Put-That-There"   44
Economy in Conversation   49
Highlights   49
Notes   50

4. Eyes as Output   **53**

Eye Actions   54
Tracking Technologies   54
Dynamic Windows: A Prototype   59
Processing Where You Look   62
The Prospects for Tracking   64
Highlights   66
Notes   66

5. The Terminal as Milieu   **69**

Virtual Solid Space   69
Overview and Immersion   71
The User as Actor   74
Nonplanar Screens   77
Highlights   78
Notes   78

6. Future Interfaces   **81**

Circumstantial Indexing   81
Multimodal Interaction   83
Self-Disclosure   86
Highlights   96
Notes   97

Bibliography   **100**

Index   **109**

List of Illustrations

Figure 2-1   The Media Room: overhead view   10

Figure 2-2   The Media Room: end view showing full display screen   11

Figure 2-3   The Media Room in use with the spatial data-management system   (Color Insert)

Figure 2-4   MIT's Dataland   (Color Insert)

Figure 2-5   The large screen functions as a magnifying glass onto Dataland   12

Figure 2-6   Zooming-in on Dataland   14

Figure 2-7   Touching the graphic book's "Table of Contents"   15

Figure 2-8   The "page-flipping" animation on the Media Room's large screen   16

Figure 2-9   How characters sent via telephone lines can merge with video graphics to become a "letter" in Dataland's mail-drop   17

Figure 2-10   Operating the "calculator" on the keymap monitor.   18

Figure 2-11   Accessing the "telephone" in Dataland   (Color Insert)

Figure 2-12   The author zooming-in on one of the TV sets in Dataland   20

Figure 2-13   Keymaps for controlling data types in Dataland   (Color Insert)

LIST OF ILLUSTRATIONS

Figure 2-14   User station for the CCA system   22

Figure 2-15   Zooming-in on ship data in the CCA system   23

Figure 2-16   CCA's system: nesting of information through ports   24

Figure 2-17   Nested country, state, and county "information space" images in the CCA system   25

Figure 2-18   The CCA spatial data-management aboard the *USS Carl Vinson*   (Color Insert)

Figure 2-19   Overlapping windows on the screen of Apple's Lisa computer: each window displays a different data set   27

Figure 2-20   Different styles of space for data   28

Figure 3-1   Speech spectrogram of a sentence   37

Figure 3-2   Patterns of pointing   42

Figure 3-3   The Nippon Electric Company (NEC) connected speech recognizer, model DP-200   43

Figure 3-4   The ROPAMS space-sensing cubes   (Color Insert)

Figure 3-5   Put-That-There   45

Figure 3-6   Put-That-There   47

Figure 3-7   Put-That-There. Deploying ships about the Caribbean Sea via speech and pointing   (Color Insert)

Figure 4-1   Eyeglass-mounted tracking   55

Figure 4-2   Diagram showing the optical path of corneal reflection from light-emitting diode (LED) to sensing photodiode array   56

Figure 4-3   The G&W Applied Science Laboratories eye-movement monitoring system (Model 1998)   58

Figure 4-4   The extended head-tracking option (EHT) on the G&W Applied Science Laboratories eye view monitor (Model 1998)   59

Figure 4-5   The "World of Windows." Up to thirty images are on display at one time   (Color Insert)

Figure 4-6   Selective development in the progressive transmission of pictures   63

Figure 5-1   Beyond the looking glass   70

Figure 5-2   The "Movie Map." Driving by videodisc about the streets of Aspen, Colorado   (Color Insert)

Figure 5-3   Typical IMAX theater   73

Figure 5-4   Typical OMNIMAX theater   74

Figure 5-5   Human animation: light-emitting diodes plus a computer translate actions into illustrations   75

Figure 5-6   The "Cloud Person" figure driven by motions of the human scriptor   76

Figure 5-7   The talking-head "persona"   (Color Insert)

Figure 6-1   Images from MIT's "Communication News" project   (Color Insert)

Figure 6-2   A multimodal command using speech, looking, and gesture   86

Figure 6-3   Record of eye movements during free examination of the photograph for three minutes   89

Figure 6-4   Spontaneous looking. Record of eye movements during free examination of the photograph for two minutes   90

Figure 6-5   Task-oriented looking. Seven records of eye movements by the same observer, each record derived from three minutes of looking at the picture at the upper left   91

Figure 6-6   Eye-tracking the user of a desktop terminal is feasible with current technology   94

Foreword

The human interface with computers is the physical, sensory, and intellectual space that lies between computers and ourselves. Like any place this space can be unfamiliar, cold, and unwelcoming. But it can also be like some other places, those we know and love, those that are familiar, comfortable, warm, and, most importantly, personal.

Currently, this space tends not to have the elements of personalization, sensory richness, and intelligence to which we are accustomed, for example, in human-to-human contact. Whereas talking to a computer should be as easy as or easier than talking to another human being whom we know intimately, with whom we have had shared experiences, in fact if we but glance at the most advanced computer systems, whether in the military, in commercial use, or in the home, we find that the use of the systems ranges from difficult to debilitating. This we can overcome only by the efforts of professional perseverence or by the relentless resilience of a child's inherent and unabashed thirst to play. Not only can the difficult and debilitating aspects of such systems discourage our use of computers in general, but worse, when we do make the effort to use them, their limited intelligence, sensory apparatus, and recognition facilities preclude our talking to them about almost anything and everything that means something to us.

This book paints a different picture. Drawn from specific experiments, the following chapters put forward examples of human interfaces populated with sensory apparatus that work in concert with each other in order to recognize human intentions and to output computer responses in a human vocabulary, one not limited to verbal languages. Richard Bolt points to recognition systems never before conceived of as regular channels of communication with computers, whereas we use such systems regularly in interpersonal communications. Who had ever thought of eyes as "output devices"? Yet we use eyes as pointers during almost every moment of face-to-face, human dialogue.

Richard Bolt's book is meant to excite, to invite the reader into different styles of thinking about the human interface. It is meant to encourage you to ask new questions and to look in new directions. The directions in which the following examples and experiments are pointing you are the opportunities of the next decade.

Nicholas Negroponte
Massachusetts Institute
of Technology

Preface

THE PURPOSE OF THIS BOOK

As computer technology and society's use of computers continue to converge ever more rapidly, so the need intensifies to achieve a *completely natural dialogue or interaction between machines and human beings.* The aim of *The Human Interface* is to examine the concepts and situations under which this desired interaction takes place or could take place.

THE THEMES

This book pursues themes that are central to any consideration of *the interface*—the place where people and computers meet. The chief themes considered are as follows:

- *spatiality* as a radically new approach to storing and retrieving data (chapter 2)
- *speech and gesture* working together in a powerful way to express commands (chapter 3)
- *eye contact* with the computer to manage a dynamic display of images (chapter 4)
- *the interface as a place*, not just a tiny porthole into data (chapter 5).

PREFACE

THE AUDIENCE

This book is for conceptualizers and designers of computer systems—both hardware and software—who need to extend their understanding of the interface. It is also for computer programmers, for engineers, architects, ergonomists, psychologists, physiologists—specifically those concerned with how computers deal with people. Students in computer science and related programs who are involved in the human/computer dialogue will also benefit from this book.

THE APPROACH

Throughout I have emphasised the main ideas, rather than transient techniques. I have presented specific examples of each concept as it relates to the interface, based on actual prototypes researched at MIT's Architecture Machine Group laboratory. I have also noted related work done elsewhere and stressed applications of that work. In considering future developments I conclude the book with a selective look at what I think will be key themes for future interfaces. At the end of every chapter, under the heading "Highlights," I have summarized the main principles considered in that chapter, whilst detailed commentary and references have been placed in the "Notes" for each chapter so as not to clutter the main text.

THE ACKNOWLEDGMENTS

The impetus for writing this book arose from my participation in human/machine interface work at MIT's Architecture Machine Group, where I helped to formulate a vision of the interface as an eminently habitable place to be. I am therefore indebted to my association with that unique laboratory, now merged into the Media Laboratory at MIT's new Center for Arts and Media Technology.

Some further notes of thanks are due. I wish to thank Professor Patrick Purcell of the Royal College of Art, London, who, while visiting at MIT, read an early draft and furnished many helpful criticisms. My thanks go also to Professor Andrew Lippman, director of the Architecture Machine Group, for permission to use photographs from the Group's collection to help illustrate this book. (Those photographs without specific accompanying acknowledgments are copyrighted by the Architecture Machine Group, MIT.) Some photographic credits are also due: to Christian Lischewski for the photographs in chapter 2 illustrating MIT's Spatial Data Management System, as well as for Figure 3-7; to Bob Mohl for Figure 5-2; and to Scott Fisher for Figure 4-6, which also appears on the book jacket. Eric Hulteen drew Figures 2-1 and 2-2.

Especial thanks are due to the people at Lifetime Learning who contributed so much to the production of this book.

Thanks also to Professor Nicholas Negroponte for his encouragement when I first undertook this project and for supplying the Foreword.

Most of all, my thanks to my wife Olga, and to my sons John and Nicky, whose love and forbearance allowed me the time to write this book.

Richard A. Bolt

The
Human Interface

WHERE PEOPLE AND
COMPUTERS MEET

1.

Where in the World Is the Information?

- *Beyond the Keyboard*
- *Using Space to Organize Data*
- *Space and Computers*
- *Highlights*

People are very good at using the space around them for organizing and storing things. They lose this option, though, when they sit down to work with computers. The opportunities and means to use space in dealing with data just aren't there. This chapter is about regaining those opportunities and means.

BEYOND THE KEYBOARD

I am using a personal computer to write this book, typing in words and sentences with the help of a special word-processing program. This program enables me to present the text I am writing on a display screen. I can insert phrases, delete them, even move whole sections of text about.

What I especially appreciate, since I tend to revise a lot as I go along, is that I can print out on paper a fresh draft of my text whenever I need it. Once I've marked up the draft, made cross-outs and additions, placed little balloons and arrows all about, I can go back to my computer and make the changes. More and more, I make such changes directly on the screen. I feel free to revise knowing I don't have to retype everything to get back to a clean, error-free copy. This is a marvelous boon to excruciatingly slow typists like me. The computer-as-word-processor is just plain wonderful. It is one of the best things ever to happen to writers.[1]

The computer is just plain wonderful but . . . .

What is less wonderful about the computer-as-writing-partner is that, as I write it, my book becomes tucked away somewhere inside the machine. What I see of the text is only what can fit at any one time on my computer's twenty-five-line display screen. There is something disconcerting about this.

I don't mean fears that the machine will gobble up all the text and throw it away. Or that the machine will inadvertently wipe out the little flexible magnetic disk files it uses to store the text of my book. That could happen. But it's unlikely, and I faithfully follow the suggested backup procedure of always writing out an extra copy of everything. And I certainly don't suffer from "cyberphobia," a new label for the irrational fear of computers.[2]

What bothers me is that I can't, on the computer, *see* my book. I can't spread it out so that I can take in its overall organization like a painter stepping back from the canvas. This is something we do to help us think about things, to see where we are in the midst of them. It's part of the "task demands," as the human-factors engineer might put it, of writing a book.

To see the overall pattern of data, we have to spread it out.

Well, I spread things out anyway. At home, our dining room table has been commandeered for the duration of this book. I have the material for each chapter—outlines, notes, papers, five-by-eight cards, articles, clippings, and so forth—stacked in file folders, one for each chapter. The folders in turn are arranged clockwise around the perimeter of the table, starting with Chapter 1 at my left elbow.

Then, about the dining room, on chairs, on the floor, on the tiny writing desk, I have books, journal articles, and yet more notes placed strategically, not in chapter order, but by topic. These stacks are not labeled in any way. I just know what things are where. And as long as I don't shift things around too much, and I replace the piles carefully when they get disturbed—as when I had to move everything out while we had company for dinner last evening—I can easily find what I need.

Now, I would have been doing all of this spreading things out even if I hadn't had the word processor to help me. It's the way I work and, I suspect, the way most people work when they have some complex task. The relevant point is that the computer doesn't help me with the larger, organizational dimension of the task. I need that support as never before precisely because my manuscript, as it grows, becomes hidden from me in a way I never experienced before.

My computer's keyboard and screen are offering me only part of what I need. It handles *text* well, but not my *book*. The interface between me and the computer may well be the keyboard and that tiny screen, but the interface between me and my writing job goes beyond my computer's keyboard and screen to include my dining room table (indeed, our whole dining room).

The computer screen handles text, not a book.

USING SPACE TO ORGANIZE DATA

Keeping track of a book by spreading it out on the dining room table is an instance of a more general principle: managing things spatially. Consider people's desktops. The appointment book is situated at the bottom and to the left. The telephone is in the upper right corner. Family pictures are above the blotter, to the left of the telephone, and so on. And maybe piles of papers lying about as well.

Let people "straighten out" things, and suddenly we can't seem to locate anything. Unwittingly, they have disturbed our memory map of where things are. Now we have to resort to deliberate searching where before a spontaneous reach would do.

Or consider my bookcase. The copy of *Moby Dick* resides on the second shelf from the top, at the far left end. When I reach for it, I do not even have to look in that direction because my action is guided automatically by a mental schema of where it's located, as well as by a sort of "motor memory" whereby my very arms and fingers seem involved in remembering where things are.[3]

Shopping in one's favorite supermarket is another case in point. Visit a strange store, and it takes much longer to find things. The mental map that lets us go directly to the desired item in our usual store is missing. Yet another example of the role of spatiality in everyday life is that of finding one's way to work and then home again. When we set out for home, we in a sense "retrieve" the place where we live.

Mental maps speed up the searching process.

Probably the first person to elevate managing information spatially to a formal technique was Simonides, a poet and teacher of rhetoric who lived in ancient Greece about 500 B.C. Having recited a heroic eulogy at the home of an Olympic wrestling victor, Simonides by sheer luck was called away outside the premises just before the accidental collapse of the banquet room floor. The host and all the guests were killed, the bodies so damaged in the resulting fire that recognition was virtually impossible. But Simonides, having observed the places in the room occupied by the various guests, was able to aid the searchers in making identification.[4]

Simonides' memory for people-in-place was not only robust but "incidental"—that is, his memory pattern formed without any deliberate effort on his part. Psychological research supports the notion that people learn readily, and without effort, the whereabouts of things in space.[5]

Simonides had discovered a powerful memory principle: the assignment of names, objects, possibly even abstract ideas, to fixed positions in space. He went on to develop a method of committing material to memory that has come to be known as the Method of Loci.[6]

Assigning data to fixed positions in space is the crux of the Method of Loci.

Simonides taught his students first to call to mind a vivid image of the floor plan of, say, a temple. The building could be either real or imaginary, but in either case it had to be highly familiar. Then, when rehearsing the opening remarks of the speech to be memorized, the student should keep in the mind's eye an image of the entrance of the temple. The more concrete the image the better: the detailing of statues, the fluting of pillars, and so forth.

Having rehearsed the preliminary remarks, the student should then proceed in the imagination on a simple, systematic path about the floor of the temple, going from niche to niche, each niche holding its statue or bust of a deity. Before each sculpture in turn, successive parts of the speech would be rehearsed. While rehearsing the remarks, the image of the current place in the temple was to be pictured vividly in the imagination.

Later, when delivering the speech, the pupils would mentally reenact their route about the temple. In imagination, they would walk up to the entrance of the temple, stop, and deliver the introductory remarks. Having completed them, they would in the mind's eye enter the temple and approach the first of the interior niches holding a statue. There they would recite the passage associated with the statue. Then they would walk to the next niche, recite the remarks associated with the statue in that spot, and so forth and so on about the temple floor. The resulting recall would invariably prove to be

4

remarkably good in spite of the students' nervousness . . . or even the collapse of a banquet hall. This simple technique, so highly effective in the school of Simonides, is still basic to tutors of *mnemonics* or memory today.[7]

SPACE AND COMPUTERS

Psychologist George A. Miller may have been the first to suggest in a computer context that data might be managed on a spatial basis. In his marvelously perceptive article, "Psychology and Information," published in 1968, he asked the leading question: "Where in the world is the information?" He meant the question quite literally, pointing out that people like to know *where* the information is.[8]

People like to know the whereabouts of data.

Elaborating his wish to know the whereabouts of data, Miller recalled that traditional libraries gave considerable thought to the spatial arrangement of information. Books on the same subject were collected together. Stacks were arranged so that the visitor could walk up and down between them, reaching up for this subject, down and to the left for another. Book spines were clearly marked; new books and special collections were in distinctive spots.

With the new modes of information storage, Miller noted, whether on microfilm or in digital store, we can no longer go directly into the storage system to take the information in hand. Instead, we must "hold a dialog with it on some console whose spatial location relative to the information is completely irrelevant to the system."[9] This of course is what is happening to my book as it becomes transformed from note cards and outlines in definite stacks about my dining room table into streams of typed characters stored away on little magnetic storage disks.

In any event, when MIT's Architecture Machine Group proposed a series of studies on multimedia interfaces to the Cybernetics Technology Office of the Defense Advanced Research Projects Agency (DARPA) in 1976, two of the studies focused on the *spatial location* of data as an organizational principle.[10] After further negotiation with DARPA on the proposal, the Architecture Machine Group was given the task of developing a "spatial data-management system." DARPA's interest was in data-management strategies that would be *easy* to learn and straightforward to operate, especially for occasional use by nonspecialists like military commanders. In the next chapter I'll explain how this spatial data-management system works and describe the special setting we built for it: our Media Room.

HIGHLIGHTS

- Word processors are superb instruments for handling information, but they don't let you see the overall pattern of organization.
- Information can be managed spatially—that is, it can be assigned to certain fixed positions in space to help us recall its location.
- Computers, unlike libraries, have a way of hiding the whereabouts of information.

NOTES

[1.] See William Zinsser, *Writing with a Word Processor* (New York: Harper & Row, 1983).

[2.] "Get Vertigo Over Video Displays? Maybe It's a Case of Cyberphobia?", *Wall Street Journal,* Tuesday, 8 June 1982, p. 37. See also "Dealing with Terminal Phobia," *Time,* 19 July 1982, p. 37.

[3.] I recall reading somewhere—the reference escapes me—that British journalist and television personality Alistair Cooke once made use of a "book map" of the United States. This was early in his career when he had just been placed on assignment in this country. Cooke placed his books about the various states so that their position on the shelf corresponded to their geographic position: Maine in the top right corner, Florida at bottom right, Alaska at top left, and so forth. Thus his mental map of America gave him direct access to the relevant volumes.

[4.] See M. L. Hunter, *Memory* (Baltimore: Penguin Books, 1957); see also F. A. Yates, *The Art of Memory* (Chicago: University of Chicago Press, 1966).

[5.] One investigator reports: "Location (i.e., position in space) seems to be an attribute that is routinely encoded, for its incidental recall is at least as good as its intentional." See Arthur I. Schulman, "Recognition Memory and the Recall of Spatial Location," *Memory and Cognition* 1(3)(1973):259. See also Jean M. Mandler, Dale Seegmiller, and Jeanne Day, "On the Coding of Spatial Information," *Mem-*

ory and Cognition 5(1)(1977):10–16; Lynn Hasher and R. T. Zacks, "Automatic and Effortful Processes in Memory," *Journal of Experimental Psychology; General* 108(1979):356–388.

6. Ulric Neisser, *Cognition and Reality* (San Francisco: Freeman, 1976), pp. 135–138.

7. See, for example, Harry Lorayne and Jerry Lucas, *The Memory Book* (New York: Ballantine Books, 1974).

8. George A. Miller, "Psychology and Information," *American Documentation* 19(3)(July 1968):286–289.

9. Ibid., p. 288.

10. Nicholas Negroponte and Richard A. Bolt, "Augmentation of Human Resources in Command and Control Through Multiple Media Man-Machine Interaction," proposal to U.S. Defense Advanced Research Projects Agency (DARPA), Office of Cybernetics Technology (Cambridge, Mass.: MIT Architecture Machine Group, 1976).

2.

The Uses of Space

- *The Media Room*
- *The World of Dataland*
- *Other Ways of Using Space*
- *Design Issues*
- *Future Developments*
- *Highlights*

We have seen that spatiality is a powerful organizational principle in everyday life—from shopping at the local supermarket to coping with a thousand complex pages of manuscript. Increasingly, therefore, computer systems will exploit our sense of space for data management and retrieval. By "spreading things out" in high-quality computer graphics space, we can see more clearly what's there: old things where we remember them, new things where we expect them to be. In this chapter we'll examine the innovative features of the Media Room and enter the compact but eminently practical world of Dataland, where a universe of information can be summoned by touch or voice command.

THE MEDIA ROOM

The Media Room at MIT's Architecture Machine Group laboratory is a setting where the room itself is the terminal.[1] The Media Room

(Figures 2-1 and 2-2) is the size of a personal office, 16 feet long, 11 feet wide, and about 8 feet from floor to ceiling. One entire end of the room is a display screen: a plate of tempered glass about 13 feet on the diagonal. The glass is frosted so that a color TV projection system situated in an adjoining space can back-project on it. The floor of the room is raised to accommodate cabling from an ensemble of minicomputers that drive displays and devices resident in the Media Room.

Here the room itself is the terminal.

The walls, floor, and ceiling of the room are a rich brown in color, intended as soothing, not somber. Overhead are three rows of recessed ceiling lights. The brightness of each row, front to back, can be modulated independently—manually by knobs at present, but conceivably by computer as well.

The user sits in a vinyl-covered Eames chair stationed at room center about 10 feet back from the room's large screen (Figure 2-3, see Color Insert). This chair is exactly as it comes from the furniture store except for two small "joysticks," each about three-fourths of an inch high, situated on either arm where the hands would normally rest. Near each joystick is a 2-inch, square-shaped, touch-sensitive pad.[2] On either side of the user's chair, and within arm's reach, are two television monitors. Their tube faces are overlaid with transparent touch-sensitive plastic sheeting, providing the system with the coordinates of the user's touch.[3]

At the heart of the room is the user's chair.

Four loudspeakers are located in front of the user, one at each corner of the wall-sized screen. An additional array of four speakers is set in the walls somewhat to the rear of the user's chair. These eight speakers enable the system to immerse the user in a world of three-dimensional sound.

The Media Room is equipped with a connected-speech recognition system. (*Connected speech* refers to speech as it naturally flows, without deliberate pauses between words.) While we have experimented with a remote "shotgun" microphone situated at a distance from the user, satisfactory speech recognition depends upon the user wearing a head-mounted, noise-canceling microphone.

THE WORLD OF DATALAND

The spatial data-management system is created by a set of color TV images presented in the Media Room setting. These images are sent over cables from a set of minicomputers in our laboratory's machine

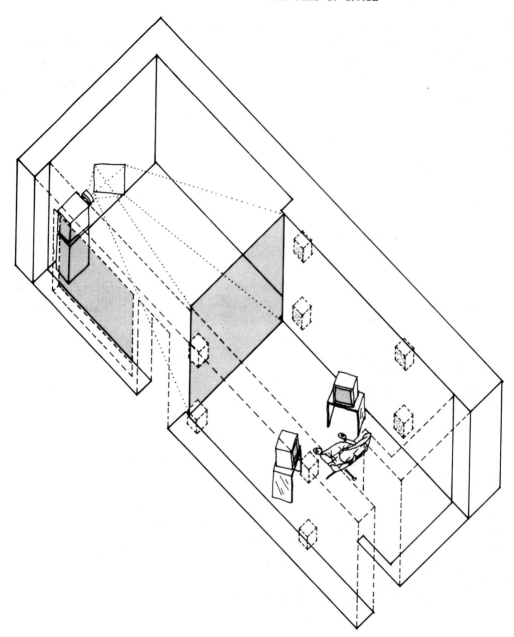

Figure 2-1. The Media Room: overhead view.

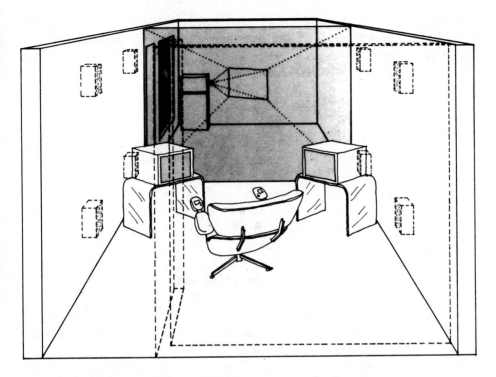

Figure 2-2. The Media Room: end view showing full display screen. (Copyright 1980, 1981, Association for Computing Machinery, Inc. Used with permission.)

room.[4] On the monitor to the user's left (or right, if preferred) is a picture of the user's data. We have dubbed this little world of data *Dataland,* and we refer to the monitor that bears it as the *worldview* monitor.

Figure 2-4 (*see* Color Insert) shows what one hypothetical user's Dataland might look like. We see tiny pictures of faces, maps, television sets, letters, book covers, a calendar, a telephone, and a calculator. In some cases, items of a similar sort are grouped together on distinctive color backgrounds.

Your personal Dataland would look different from mine or anyone else's. There would be different items in different arrangements, just as the everyday desktops of people reflect their individuality. What would be common to all Datalands, however, is that the data types dwelling in them would be presented as images in specific locations.

Dataland's contents reflect the individual user.

Dataland isn't a map of the data; it is the data.

Importantly, the items in Dataland are *facsimile* in nature: books look like books, calendars like calendars, and so on. Dataland is not a map of the data. It *is* the data. The nature of the display is "out there," visually self-evident.

The user's current location in Dataland is portrayed at all times on the worldview monitor by a small translucent overlay: a "you-are-here" marker covering a subsection of about one sixty-fourth of Dataland's area. (See the lower left-hand corner of Figure 2-4.) The subsector of Dataland indicated by this small translucent square is shown to the user, enlarged and enhanced in detail, on the wall-sized screen. Thus the logical relationship of the large screen to the worldview monitor is as a movable "magnifying glass" or magnifying window onto Dataland (Figure 2-5).

Locating Data in Dataland

The user navigates about the Dataland surface in a helicopter-like fashion by means of the joystick on the right arm of the chair. Pushing this joystick to the left causes the small rectangular "you-are-here" overlay marker on the worldview monitor to move to the left. Simultaneously, the corresponding magnified portion of Dataland goes scudding by to the right on the large screen.[5]

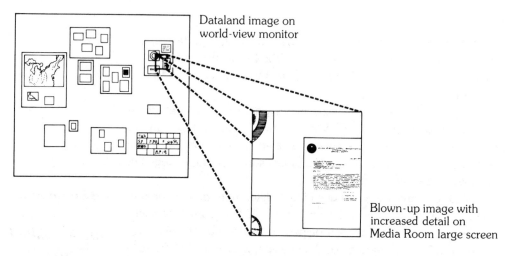

Dataland image on world-view monitor

Blown-up image with increased detail on Media Room large screen

Figure 2-5. The large screen functions as a magnifying glass onto Dataland.

Another way of getting about Dataland is by "touch travel" on the touch-sensitive surface of the worldview monitor. The user simply touches the desired spot on Dataland. On the big screen, the magnified image of the current location disappears, to be replaced by a view of the Dataland surface at the destination point. Correspondingly, the translucent "you-are-here" marker on the worldview monitor disappears from its old spot and appears at the new one.

A third way to travel about Dataland is by "voice travel." The user asks the system to be taken somewhere—for example, "Take me to the calculator." As with touch travel, the "you-are-here" marker shifts appropriately, and the image of the current location on the large screen disappears . . . to be replaced, in this case, with a large image of Dataland's calculator.

The user navigates Dataland by joystick, by touch command, or by voice.

In voice travel, the user can readily take advantage of *relational* expressions—as for example in the command "Take me to the map . . . above and to the left of the calculator." The layout of Dataland gives users the opportunity to express themselves by using "here" and "there" or "above" and "below" or "left," "right," and "middle" or "to the northeast" and so forth. Items can thus be referenced with respect to each other or in terms of their position in Dataland.

Perusing Data in Dataland

Perusing any data type, once you have found it in Dataland, depends on the kind of data type it is. Because the data in Dataland are *facsimile*—in the spirit of "what you see is what you get"—the style of perusal is in most cases exactly what one would expect: Perusing a book means turning its pages; using a calculator means pressing its buttons; and so on.

Data types range from books to maps to telephone.

First the user must approach the item. Pushing forward on the left-hand joystick causes a zooming-in upon the image on the large screen (Figure 2-6). Pulling back on the joystick causes a zooming back out again.

With most data types, perusal is aided by a display that comes up on the other, as yet unused, monitor to the user's right (or left). These displays—touch-sensitive and in some instances voice-activated as well—are what we call *keymaps*. Their function will become clearer as we review the data types that inhabit Dataland in the following sections.

13

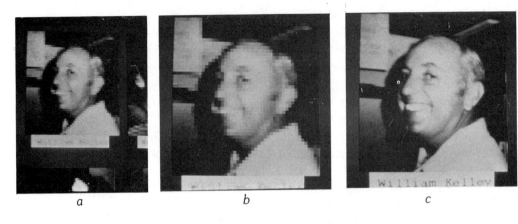

a *b* *c*

Figure 2-6a,b,c. Zooming-in on Dataland. The zooming-in effect is achieved by a special computer-graphics technique. The image is composed of an array of tiny dots called pixels (for "picture elements"). Pressing forward on the left joystick signals the system to begin to repeat—in the sense of "showing again"—these pixels in both the horizontal and vertical direction from center image on outward. *(a)* As the image expands it becomes increasingly indistinct, as the pixel-repetition process merely "stretches" whatever picture information was already there and doesn't add new detail. The "blocky" look is due to the squarish pattern of pixel repetitions. *(b)* While scaling up the image, the system obtains from magnetic disk storage a fresh, detailed image at the same scale and registration as the blocky one. Switching the system's display processor to the new image instantly clarifies the visible picture for the user. *(c)* This stepwise process might be repeated several times in succession where great magnification of the image is called for. The process of zooming-out is simply a reversal of this procedure.

Books. There are two different "book sections" in our Dataland. One section, with a buff-colored background, holds technical books and is situated in the central portion of Dataland. The other section, for leisure or general reading, is in the south central part of Dataland and has a blue background color (Figure 2-4, Color Insert).

Zooming in on the cover of one of the books causes its table of contents to come up on the touch-sensitive monitor to the user's right. Simultaneously, the first page of the book—or the page where you last left off reading it—comes up on the Media Room's large screen. Touching any major chapter heading on the right-hand mon-

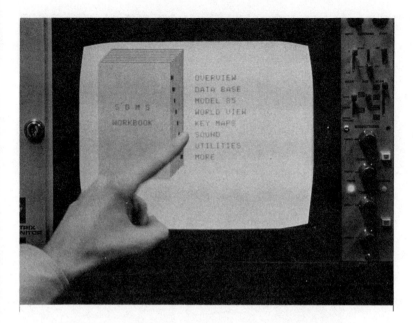

Figure 2-7. Touching the graphic book's "Table of Contents."
(See also the lower left quadrant of Figure 2-13.)

itor produces a breakdown of that chapter by subheadings on the screen (Figure 2-7).

As the user goes from section to section, a page-flipping animation on the large screen bridges the time between the appearance of the initial pages of each section selected. The amount of flipping action is proportional to the number of pages passed by between sections; the direction of flipping is determined by whether the user is going forward or backward in the book (Figure 2-8).

On the large screen, individual pages of the book may be turned forward by means of a top-right to bottom-left finger stroke on either of the small touch-sensitive pads mounted in the arms of the user's chair. The same computer-graphics technique that underlies the flipping sequence now creates a visual effect of the current page being "peeled away" to reveal the next numbered page. This page-turning animation visually separates one page from the next and gives readers a sense of where they are in the material in a way that endlessly scrolled text would not.[6] A finger stroke on either of the small touch pads, now in the bottom-left to top-right direction, serves to turn a

Flipping pages conveys a sense of where you are in the material.

15

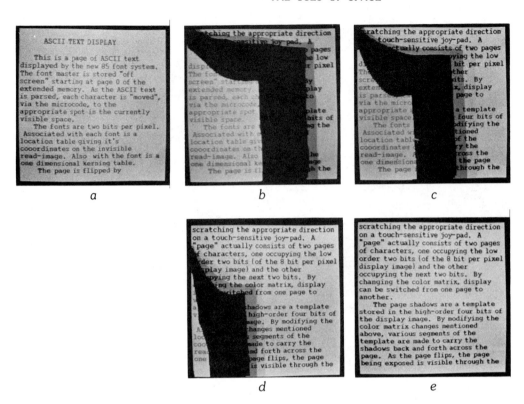

Figure 2-8a,b,c,d,e. The "page-flipping" animation on the Media Room's large screen.

page back—now the page-turning visual effect goes in the opposite direction.

The books themselves, denoted by their graphic "covers" in Dataland, exist offscreen as streams of alphanumeric characters stored on magnetic disk. To users, a strange cover appearing some morning in either book area may represent a best-seller or a new technical text that arrived overnight as characters over telephone lines, now to be read at leisure, composed page by page in high-quality television text on the large screen before them.[7]

Facsimile letters appear with their own letterheads and logos.

Letters. Letters appear in Dataland's mail area in the northeast. A letter may be read by simply zooming in and reading it. Like the book data type, the text of the letter may have just arrived over telephone lines as a stream of characters. The sender's identifying letterhead or logo is retrieved when possible from a cache of locally

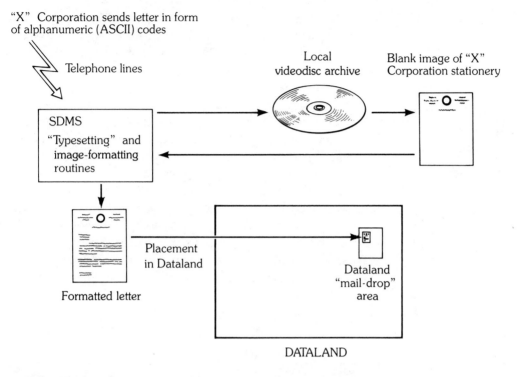

"X" Corporation sends letter in form
of alphanumeric (ASCII) codes

Telephone lines

Local
videodisc archive

Blank image of "X"
Corporation stationery

SDMS

"Typesetting" and
image-formatting
routines

Placement
in Dataland

Formatted letter

Dataland
"mail-drop"
area

DATALAND

**Figure 2-9. How characters sent via telephone lines can
merge with video graphics to become a "letter" in Dataland's
mail-drop.**

stored letterhead images. With that letterhead image as "stationery,"
the system would then compose the letter and place it in the "letter
drop" in the upper right corner of Dataland (Figure 2-9). Even at
reduced scale, distinctive letterheads stand out. Urgent or eagerly
awaited letters might be "blinked" or otherwise signaled to the user's
attention.

Maps.   Maps on Dataland—there are several at the upper left—
become greatly magnified as the user zooms in upon them. At any
level of approach during zooming, the user may travel by joystick
about the map image. The map, of course, has a natural affinity for
storage on the Dataland surface. Any map may·in turn be itself used
as a kind of internal Dataland—as, for example, organizing sales
force data geographically by sales office location or by sales region.

17

The Calculator. Interacting with the "calculator" means using it to calculate. Zooming in upon it on the large screen causes a working version to be brought up on the keymap monitor (Figure 2-10). It operates by finger contact just like an actual calculator. One might conceivably ask the system via its speech recognizer, for example, "What is the square root of 51?" and get the answer either posted on the large screen or recited via synthesized speech output.[8] However, the user might well prefer the more ruminative mode of picking out the computations on the displayed touch-sensitive calculator.

The calculator, trivial by itself, gains importance as an instance of a greater class of data types: *processes*. Processes activated and controlled by pushbutton devices—from food blenders to air conditioners to powerplant consoles—are all about us, in homes, offices, and industry. Control panels can readily be created in color computer graphics. They can be made touchable by touch-sensitive overlays and perhaps voice-addressable as well by speech-recognition technology.

Imagine that you are a marketing manager in a corporation that

> *The calculator could respond to either voice or touch.*

Figure 2-10. Operating the "calculator" on the keymap monitor.

specializes in control systems. You have just been sent a working model of a proposed new design to try out and offer comments and criticisms. What you are sent, however, is not a physical model but an electronic facsimile whose panel image, design schematics, and underlying operating logic have been sent to you over telephone lines. In fact any *process* might be sent in this way, perusable in Dataland, as is this tiny calculator, via touch and voice.

The Telephone. Zooming in upon Dataland's telephone image brings up a telephone control panel on the right-hand monitor (Figure 2-11, *see* Color Insert). There are three ways to place a call. One way is by touch-dialing upon a set of virtual pushbuttons in the same spirit as manipulation of the calculator. Another is to locate the name of the party on an alphabetical list of persons frequently called. This list slides by, under touch control, on a small vertical "window" on the telephone keymap. Names and addresses appear with work and home phone numbers. Touching a number initiates a call to that number.

Three ways of placing a call: touch dialing, touch control, and voice command.

Yet a third way to initiate a telephone call is simply to ask the system: "Connect me with Mr. Henry Williams . . . at his office." If the sound pattern "Henry Williams" exists in the speech recognizer's files, the system will place the call—in this instance to Mr. Williams' business number, not his home phone.

Film. Yet another data type is the *filmic sequence.* "Filmic" means movie-like, but the term further includes material from such sources as the optical videodisk, which can show video at varying speeds in both forward and reverse, can freeze a single frame, and, unlike movie film and videotape, can offer random access to images as well as sequential access.

Dataland offers random access to images as well as sequential access.

Centrally located in Dataland are two tiny TV sets. Upon zooming in on either, the TV comes alive with dynamic movement, the system suddenly switching—at maximum zoom-in—to images from videodisk (Figure 2-12).

The associated keymap for controlling this filmic data type is shown in Figure 2-13 (*see* Color Insert). It takes the form of a clock-like figure whose circumference represents the duration of the episode to be seen, whether five seconds or three hours. Touching anywhere on the clock's edge results in direct access to the episode at a time proportional to the point you touch on the 360-degree circumference.

19

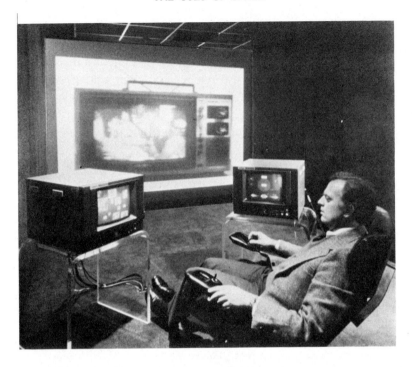

Figure 2-12. The author zooming-in on one of the TV sets in Dataland.

This random-access feature is of course highly compatible with the optical videodisk as storage medium, given the disk's capacity to seek forward or in reverse to any specific frame. A touch facility to "dog-ear" any part of the episode produces a graphic "spike" in the clock's perimeter; touching the spike at any time readdresses the filmic episode to that point. A forward/backward arrow on the key-map permits the user to indicate variable-speed forward/reverse play, and graphic buttons allow single-step viewing and freeze frames.

When facsimiles are realistic, the user knows how to react.

Familiarity Breeds Content. In general, then, the data types in Dataland occupy a spatial arrangement highly familiar to the user. Retrieval of data means going to where it is in Dataland. Interaction with data types—what we call *perusal*—means having data types as realistic as possible so that the user will know intuitively how to interact with them.

Not included in our version of Dataland is an alphanumeric keyboard. It was deliberately left out to emphasize the alternative

20

ways of dealing with data. I, of course, would need one in there—a lap model—to write my book. I would be typing in my paragraphs and my text would be appearing on the big screen in well-formed fonts. I would place each developing section and chapter in special spots within my "book-in-progress" area. Alas, a working lab cannot offer such a luxury. Meanwhile, I have my dining room table.

Ease of Learning

What about one of the original goals in constructing Dataland: a system that a novice or occasional user could handle without undue difficulty?

In our experience with the many guest users—numbering in the hundreds—who have come into our Media Room to see a live demonstration of the system and try it out personally, one thing stood out. People became entirely capable of operating the system themselves in well under one minute. Almost immediately their main concern became *what* information was there to look at, not how to get at it.

In less than a minute, users feel at home in Dataland.

With the keymaps, the spontaneous intuitions of guest users generally served them well. The impulse to stab a finger at the keys of the touch-dial telephone was valid, for instance, as was the urge to touch chapter headings in the displayed book. Guests had to be shown—once—how to turn the book's pages. It is not intuitively obvious that you can "turn the pages" of a color TV screen. Once the forward turning was demonstrated, however, the way to turn pages back was readily guessed.

OTHER WAYS OF USING SPACE

Other systems have been developed to exploit graphic space.[9] I will not review them in detail here but will focus instead on the ways in which they use space.

CCA's System

About a year into its sponsorship of the spatial data-management project at MIT, DARPA commissioned Computer Corporation of America (CCA) of Cambridge, Massachusetts, to build a "field

21

version" of a spatial data-management system. Initially modeled on leads established at MIT, in time the work at CCA developed its own emphases and directions.[10]

CCA's system has three color TV monitors lined up on a table-top (Figure 2-14). The monitors at either end are equipped with touch-sensitive screens. There is a single, large-knobbed joystick mounted on a boxlike base. The right-hand monitor has a keyboard. A graphic data tablet is included primarily for editing images.

CCA's system has two styles of space.

Spatially, CCA's system functions in two styles. The first style is essentially equivalent to the MIT system just described. The leftmost screen holds a high-level or worldview image of the database. A highlighted, translucent "you-are-here" rectangle indicates the user's position on the worldview image. The single joystick control permits users to change their position on the worldview. Pressing in any direction causes the highlighted rectangle to move in that direction. The highlighted portion of the worldview is shown magnified on the screen of the center or main display monitor (analogous to the Media Room's large screen). Twisting the handle of the joystick clockwise causes zooming-in. As the user zooms in closer upon some item on the data surface, the item gains increasing detail (Figure 2-15). Twisting the joystick counterclockwise causes zooming-out.

The other spatial style involves not just a single data surface or *information space* (analogous to MIT's Dataland) but an entire set of them. The transition points between different information spaces

Figure 2-14. User station for the CCA system. (Photo courtesy of Computer Corporation of America, Cambridge, Massachusetts.)

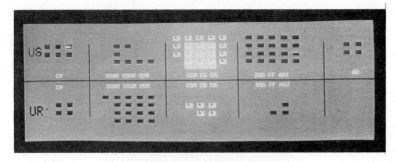

a

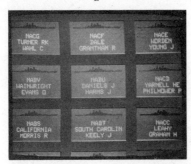

b

c   *d*

Figure 2-15a,b,c,d. Zooming-in on ship data in the CCA system. *(a)* World View of ship file with highlighted "you-are-here" marker (left screen). *(b)* Close-up of ship data (center screen). *(c)* Zooming-in on the ship "Nabu" (center screen). *(d)* Zoomed-in yet further (center screen), with appearance of detailed ship data upon near approach. (Photos courtesy of Computer Corporation of America, Cambridge, Massachusetts.)

are called *ports*. When the user zooms in on them, these ports act as trapdoors down into other information spaces (Figure 2-16).

At each step down through a port, an image of the new information-space surface comes up on the left-hand worldview monitor,

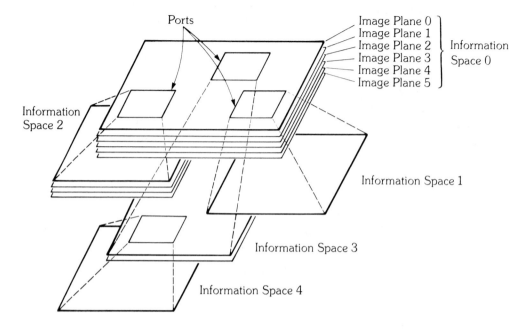

Figure 2-16. CCA's system: nesting of information through ports. Each information space is like another Dataland. *The image planes* within an information space represent successive stages of possible zooming-in on the information within that space. (Illustration adapted from Herot *et al*, 1981, with permission.)

replacing the image of the information space that was just left. The result is a hierarchical set of information spaces (Datalands) through which the user can plunge, pursuing some topic from plane to plane. Figure 2-17 presents a concrete example of this second style of using space.[11]

What distinguishes the CCA system is its ability to automatically generate a spatial image of selected portions of an extensive *alphanumeric* data base.[12] It permits, for example, the user to select which subportions of a comprehensive data base of naval ship data are to be displayed in graphics. The user can request, via keyboard, that

The position of data itself can convey information.

both U.S. and USSR ship data be formatted graphically in an information space, as seen in Figure 2-15. The request can be qualified— for example, asking for only those ships with the topmost readiness rating to be displayed. The placement of data, their internal arrangement, can convey information: ships grouped by nationality and type; oil wells by geographic drilling site. A data base of personnel

24

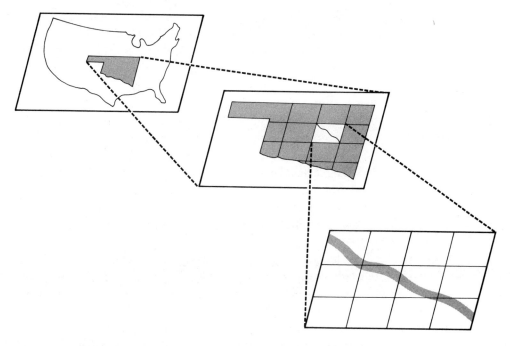

Figure 2-17. Nested country, state, and county "information space" images in the CCA system. (Illustration adapted from Herot *et al*, 1981, with permission.)

files might be laid out by years of service on the horizontal axis and by salary on the vertical axis, leading us to expect the new clerk in the lower left and senior vice-presidents to the upper right.

Accordingly, the appearance of the information space is not constant; it varies as a function of the user's typed-in request. In this use of spatiality, the expectation of where certain items will appear is based less upon memories of where you saw them before than upon *anticipations*, based on logic, as to where they ought to appear.

A working version of CCA's spatial data-management system has been installed on the United States nuclear carrier *Carl Vinson* (Figure 2-18, *see* Color Insert).

Xerox's Star, Apple's Lisa

Both Xerox's Star and Apple's Lisa are descendants of the Smalltalk system developed at Xerox's Palo Alto Research Center.

*Items can be
stacked on the
display screen
like documents
on a desktop.*

While these are not spatial data-management systems in the sense previously discussed, they do involve the placement of stacks of items on the display screen, like piles of papers on a desktop.[13]

These systems have monochromatic screen displays (high-resolution bit-mapped graphics), a keyboard, and a device called a *mouse*. A mouse is a small plastic box on a cord that can be pushed about on a desktop to control the position of a small cursor on the display screen, enabling the user to point at displayed items.[14]

A prominent feature of these systems is the use on the screen of *windows*: rectangular divisions of the screen, each displaying a different information set. There can be several tasks in progress, each task represented by its own window. The user can switch from window to window, using the mouse to point to the window that is currently to be activated.

Systems that use windows have their drawbacks, however, for the windows quickly multiply to fill the display screen. In Smalltalk, the windows were allowed to *overlap*, a feature carried over into Star and Lisa.[15] Partly covered windows peek out from behind the windows above them (Figure 2-19). With the mouse, the user can move the screen cursor over to the corner or edge of a partly covered window, press a button on the mouse, and uncover the window— that is, the window now appears lying on top of the others. The strategy of overlapping the windows is economical on screen space while producing the display counterpart of a stack of papers on one's desk. The tie-in with managing data spatially is that "stacking" is just what we do when we have lots of papers and a desk of finite size. We tend to remember—at least over the short term—what is buried in the pile, roughly where it is, and how deep.

DESIGN ISSUES

*The
presentation
style depends
on the data
and also the
user.*

We have seen three types of spatial data worlds: a large single surface, a system with ports to yet other surfaces, and a small surface on which you can pile things up (Figure 2-20). Other styles of space are possible.[16] Which style is best for which type of data? For which type of user? For which task? To offer specific guidelines is beyond the scope of this book. But two issues stand out: whether your Dataland is for your use only and whether the experience of traveling about a Dataland is coherent or not. Suppose we examine these issues in greater detail.

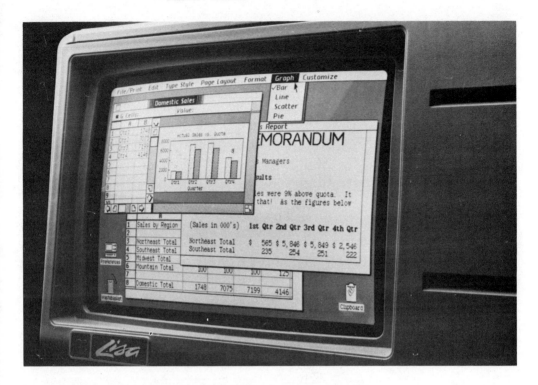

Figure 2-19. Overlapping windows on the screen of Apple's Lisa computer: each window displays a different data set.
(Photo courtesy of Apple Computer, Inc.)

Personal vs. Shared Datalands

If it is your own Dataland, and only you use it, then it can be as messy as you can stand. Though others may not be able to find anything, you will do just fine. You can even have trick items in your Dataland, the graphic counterparts of little cannons that are really cigar lighters, books that are really brandy decanters. But if the Dataland is to be shared somehow by others, then more conventional, widely shared imagery—among you and your cohorts at least—will make things easier, as will spatial consistency.[17]

Visual Continuity

In the case of Datalands that are shared with others, it is important that you and they not get disoriented because of discontinuous

27

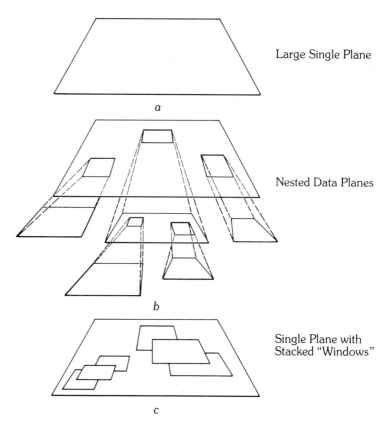

Large Single Plane

a

Nested Data Planes

b

Single Plane with
Stacked "Windows"

c

Figure 2-20. Different styles of space for data. A large single
surface *(a)*, a system with nested ports *(b)*, and a surface with stacked
information *(c)*.

imagery. That could happen if, for example, your Dataland has multiple layers. There is at least a momentary discontinuity at the moment you pop down to the next data layer. Depending on the logical
and visual sense that a data set may make against the spatial framework in which it is set, this move could—if badly managed—disori-
ent the user. Whether the transition is confusing depends particularly
on *visual continuity* (or the lack thereof) as you go from one layer to
the next.[18]

The transitions through successive ports down to the lower
planes may be visually and logically plausible, like the cuts in a well-
edited movie. Or the transitions may be hopelessly confusing. It may
help to look to cinematography for guidance. Movie makers have
developed keen skills in making cuts from viewpoint to viewpoint
within a scene and from scene to scene.[19]

*Visual
continuity
ensures
coherence.*

FUTURE DEVELOPMENTS

Let me speculate about what new directions spatial data-management might take. The spaces I have described have been flat surfaces: two-dimensional space. (Two-and-one-half dimensional, if you count zooming in and out as somehow comprising part of a dimension.) Future systems, however, could offer three-dimensional, solid spaces in which we could place data items. Whether the precise technology is holography, stereoscopy, or something else is unclear (and for now unimportant). I am thinking of cases where the data types themselves are inherently three-dimensional: data bases of sculpture, of auto design models, of cutaway views of ocean oil rigs.

A next step is three dimensions.

Another direction is the elaboration of "personal spaces" in which you can deploy things (items of data) in a lavish use of "virtual" graphic space. The essence of this approach is to create within a room such as the Media Room yet other fictitious rooms and spaces—many of them—to store all the images you'd care to. Perhaps all four walls are screens that allow you to be now in this room, now in that room, through the magic of projected graphics. Each room might be library-like, in its own way distinct, filled with finely bound books and magnificent pictures, a Dataland dispersed about fictitious premises where you can go from room to room by joysticking through the doorway images.

As computing becomes more cross-cultural in nature—right now it's concentrated in a few high-tech countries—we may well find interesting modulations of spatial data-management as a function of cultural and linguistic differences.[20] People of other cultures may not be familiar with the paper forms or concepts in computer data-management we know as "files" and "records." They may want to keep things for later but have no sense of "filing them away." A Dataland imaged in their own cultural norms might provide a compatible, plausible place for their computer to keep the things they create and to get them back—or return to them—later.

Datalands might take different forms in different cultures.

HIGHLIGHTS

- In the Media Room the user governs the flow of information from a centrally located chair. The room itself is the terminal.
- Although each Dataland reflects the individuality of the user, the data types are always presented as images in specific locations.

- Retrieval of data means going to where it is in Dataland: by using the joystick, by means of the touch-sensitive surface of the world-view monitor, or by vocal command.
- Dataland's success depends on realistic facsimiles of data in a spatial arrangement that is above all familiar to the user.
- In other systems data can be nested in sets (the CCA approach) or stacked on the display screen (the Smalltalk approach).
- Without visual continuity the system may degenerate into a muddle of imagery. Data must always make sense in their spatial framework.
- Future Datalands may exploit three-dimensional images and even assume forms befitting the cultures in which they evolve.

NOTES

[1.] The ensuing description of the Media Room is based upon Richard A. Bolt, *Spatial Data-Management* (Cambridge, Mass.: MIT Architecture Machine Group, 1979). For an expanded version of the significance of the Media Room, see Nicholas Negroponte, "Media Room," *Proceedings of the Society for Information Display* 22(2)(1981):109–113.

[2.] The small touch-sensitive pads were made by I Incorporated, 735 Addison Street, Berkeley, CA 94710.

[3.] The touch-sensitive screen position sensors were made by Eliographics, Inc., 1976 Oak Ridge Turnpike, Oak Ridge, TN 37830.

[4.] In color TV, the image is "painted" on the screen by electronic circuitry in a succession of horizontal scan lines across the face of the tube from top to bottom, thirty times per second. (In American standard TV, there are 525 such scan lines.) In TV computer graphics, the momentary color values on the scan lines are modulated not by signals coming over the airwaves, as in the case of broadcast TV, but instead by a stream of numerical values read out rapidly from a section of computer memory called a *frame buffer* or *frame store*. Up to 250,000 such eight-bit binary numbers, called *bytes*, may be used to describe a TV image at full screen resolution. Each byte corresponds one-on-one with each of the tiny color dots or *pixels* (for "picture elements") which, in mosaic, makeup the color image.

For further information on color TV computer graphics, interested readers might consult James D. Foley and Andries Van Dam, *Fundamentals of Interactive Computer Graphics* (Reading, Mass.: Addison-Wesley, 1982); see also *The Raster Graphics Handbook,* published in 1980 by Conrac Division, Conrac Corporation, 600 North Rimsdale Avenue, Covina, CA 91722.

5. In our system, the scene on the large screen moves *opposite* to the direction the joystick is pushed. This relative movement, termed *windowing,* is akin to the experience of peering through a telescope as you move it across the sky. The other option, namely to have the large screen image move in the direction the joystick is pushed, is termed *scrolling.* Visually it is akin to peering through a microscope: When you push a microscope slide to the left, the image also moves leftward.

In a study by Bury and colleagues, the windowing mode was preferred by a majority (79 percent) of novice users tested. These users were also faster on certain experimental tasks with windowing than with scrolling. See Kevin F. Bury, James M. Boyle, and Alan S. Neal, "Windowing vs. Scrolling on a Visual Display Terminal," in *Proceedings, Human Factors in Computer Systems* (New York: Association for Computing Machinery, 1982).

6. With *paging,* the presented information changes all at once; with *scrolling,* the text moves up or down the screen, whether continuously (pan scroll) or line by line (roll scroll). Given a choice, paging through displayed text seems to be preferred by novice users over scrolling. See Elmar Schwarz, Ion P. Beldie, and Seigmund Pastoor, "A Comparison of Paging and Scrolling for Changing Screen Contents by Inexperienced Users," *Human Factors* 25(3)(1983):279–282.

7. Further enhancing the readability of the books, letters, and documents in Dataland is TV text set in special *soft fonts,* which avoid the blocky, "Navaho-rug" look all too common in TV text. See Nicholas Negroponte, "Soft Fonts," paper presented at the Society for Information Display Symposium, 28 April–2 May 1980, San Diego. See also Christopher Schmandt, "Soft Typography," *Information Processing '80* (New York: North-Holland, 1980), pp. 1027–1032; Christopher Schmandt, "Greyscale Fonts Designed from Video Analysis," *Proceedings of the National Computer Graphics Association* (Fairfax, Va.: National Computer Graphics Association, 1983); John E. Warnock, "The Display of Characters Using Gray Level Sample Arrays," *Computer Graphics* 14(3)(1980):302–307.

Is it reasonable to read a book—as opposed to short sections of text—on a TV screen? Researchers at the Communications Research Center in Ottawa, Canada, seem to think so. In testing the feasibility of reading text on a television screen for extended periods, say for two hours, Muter and colleagues found that experimental subjects experienced little nausea or headache whether reading from a television screen or from a traditional book. A small amount of dizziness, fatigue, and eyestrain was produced by reading, but the differences between the amounts caused by video and by books were not statistically significant. There was no difference in comprehension scores between video reading and book reading.

The video readers read about 25 percent more slowly than the book readers. The researchers speculate that this difference might be traced to several causes: greater familiarity with books; differential effects of number of words per page (or characters per line) in the two media; posture; the fact that the video screen was still filling up with text when the book reader commenced reading the page; some combination of these reasons; or yet other reasons.

The overall conclusion, however, was that extended reading of prose, say a novel, on a television screen was indeed feasible. See Paul Muter, Susane A. Latrémouille, and William C. Treurniet, "Extended Reading of Continuous Text on Television Screens," *Human Factors* 24(5)(1982):501–508. For an assessment of the stress associated with video terminal viewing, see Michael J. Smith, Barbara G. F. Cohen, and Lambert W. Stammerjohn, Jr., "An Investigation of Health Complaints and Job Stress in Video Display Viewing," *Human Factors* 23(4)(1981):387–400.

8. For speech output, we have been utilizing the Votrax Personal Speech System, a speech synthesizer made by Votrax, 500 Stephanson Highway, Troy, MI 48084, as well as prerecorded human voice.

9. Systems have been developed that employ certain kinds of *metaphorical* space rather than offering an image of space in computer graphics. Examples include Bennett's "Negotiated Search Facility" at IBM Research in San Jose, California, and Nievergelt and Weydert's XS-O system in Switzerland. Such systems are beyond the scope of this book.

In his article on spatiality and computers, Miller comments that "the spatial orientation of the display surface really doesn't matter. What is important is the system of spatial imagery to which we refer the information on the display surface." See Miller, "Psychology and

Information," p. 288. Miller cites the case of seeing TV news segments broadcast from, say, first Saigon and then London. We don't confuse the two places, he says, but refer them to our "prior imagery" (mental map) of world geography. Thus Miller's definition of spatial systems would encompass the systems of Bennett and others.

Miller was writing in 1968, however, when good computer graphics were not as generally available as they are now. At that point in time, to have *insisted* on graphically based systems would have been unrealistic. Moreover, while most of us have a serviceable image of world geography, it may be significantly more arduous to follow other, less widely shared, spatial metaphors—particularly with a computer that is able only to talk about them, not *show* them. In any event, the focus in this book is on systems that use graphics to show the user the spaces that are involved.

The interested reader should see John L. Bennett, "Spatial Concepts as an Organizing Principle for Interactive Bibliographic Search," in Donald E. Walker (ed.), *Interactive Bibliographic Search: The User/Computer Interface* (Montvale, N.J.: AFIPS Press, 1971); J. Nievergelt and J. Weydert, "Sites, Modes, and Trails: Telling the User of an Interactive System Where He Is, What He Can Do, and How to Get to Places," in Richard A. Guedj and others (eds.), *Methodology of Interaction* (New York: North-Holland, 1980), pp. 327–338.

10. This condensed description of CCA's system is based on Christopher F. Herot, Richard Carling, Mark Friedell, David Kramlich, and Ronni L. Rosenberg, "Overview of the Spatial Data Management System," Technical Report CCA-81-08, November 1981, Computer Corporation of America, Four Cambridge Center, Cambridge, MA 02142; Christopher F. Herot, "Spatial Management of Data," *ACM Transactions on Database Systems* 5(4)(December 1980):493–514.

11. This example, with illustrations, is adapted from Herot and others, "Overview."

12. For the nonspecialist, an *alphanumeric* data base is what most of us think of when we hear the term *data*: not images, but masses of words and numbers (hence alphanumeric). For a discussion of this development in the CCA system, see Herot and others, "Overview." See also Mark Friedell, Jane Barnett, and David Kramlich, "Context-Sensitive, Graphic Presentation of Data," *Computer Graphics* 16(3)(July 1982):181–188.

[13.] See *BYTE's* special "language issue" on Smalltalk, particularly Larry Tesler, "The Smalltalk Environment," *BYTE* 6(8)(August 1981):90–147. On Xerox's Star system, see David Canfield Smith and others, "Designing the Star User Interface," *BYTE* 7(4)(April 1982):242–282. On Apple's Lisa, see Gregg Williams, "The Lisa Computer System," *BYTE* 8(2)(February 1983):33–50; George Stewart, "A First Look at Lisa," *Popular Computing* 2(5)(March 1983):84–92.

[14.] Phil Lopiccola, "Meet the Mouse," *Popular Computing* 2(5)(March 1983):102–105.

[15.] Tesler, "Smalltalk Environment," p.84. Star and Lisa apparently differ in what kind of images are allowed to overlap. See Chris Morgan, "An Interview with Wayne Posing, Bruce Daniels, and Larry Tesler," *BYTE* 8(3)(February 1983):108.

[16.] For example, a Dataland need not necessarily have edges. In certain contexts it might be useful as well as interesting for a Dataland to possess, say, a lower and leftmost edge but to be of "infinite" (indeterminate) extent otherwise.

[17.] See Thomas S. Tullis, "An Evaluation of Alphanumeric, Graphic, and Color Information Displays," *Human Factors* 23(5)(1981):549.

[18.] David D. Woods, "Visual Momentum: A Concept to Improve the Cognitive Coupling of Person and Computer," *International Journal of Man-Machine Studies,* in press.

[19.] Julian Hochberg and Virginia Brooks, "Film Cutting and Visual Momentum," in John W. Senders, Dennis F. Fisher, and Richard A. Monty (eds.), *Eye Movements and the Higher Psychological Processes* (Hillsdale, N.J.: Erlbaum Associates, 1978).

[20.] Rix Pinxten, Ingrid van Dooren, and Frank Harvey, *Anthropology of Space* (Philadelphia: University of Pennsylvania Press, 1983).

3.

Speech and Gesture

- *Machines That Recognize Speech*
- *Speech and Context*
- *When Gesture Is Gesture*
- *Capturing Speech in the Media Room*
- *Capturing Gesture in the Media Room*
- *"Put-That-There"*
- *Economy in Conversation*
- *Highlights*

What we hear currently about speech recognition by machine at the human/systems interface is that it is "not quite here yet," that it lies somewhere off in the future. From experts in the field come assertions to the effect that "mere elaboration and extrapolation of current technology will not lead to the development of machines that match the human capacity for recognizing speech. Major progress depends upon new discoveries."[1]

Designing a machine that recognizes human speech is a challenging task. The difficulties involved should not be underestimated. But two points may be ventured. The first is that useful speech at the interface may already be here in ways that are as yet not generally recognized. The second is that one of the essential "new discoveries" may in effect be an appreciation of how modalities other than speech can significantly aid in the use and interpretation of speech at the interface.

MACHINES THAT RECOGNIZE SPEECH

To anyone who has never seen a demonstration of automatic speech recognition equipment, the fact that a machine can recognize human speech at all is nothing short of amazing. Let us examine how this recognition can occur.

What Recognizers Do

Recognizers compare speech samples against their stored vocabulary.

In automatic recognizers, the standard method of word recognition employs pattern-matching techniques to compare a speech waveform sample to a collection of stored *word reference patterns*. These stored word reference patterns—constituting the machine's active vocabulary—must first be trained to the machine, however, by being spoken to the machine, one by one, while it is in *training mode.*[2]

The sound wave for each word is then sampled, say, every 25 milliseconds by a bank of octave filters covering the frequency range of about 250 to 5000 hertz (cycles per second). The result is an array: The horizontal axis is *time*, the vertical axis *frequency*. Each cell of the array contains a number reflecting the amplitude of sound at that moment and centering around that frequency. The total collection of arrays thus formed for each word as it is trained makes up the active vocabulary of the machine (see Figure 3-1).

When the machine is put into *recognition mode*, the input speech signal is similarly analyzed for its momentary frequency spectrum, creating an array or template for the just-uttered word. This template is matched against the collection of templates that constitute the active vocabulary of the machine, perhaps on the order of from fifty to one hundred words. In this comparison process, compressing and stretching out stored templates may be done according to an optimization process called *dynamic programming* in order to take into account differences in how rapidly the same person may articulate the same word on different occasions. Such prolongations or contractions in pronunciation can be quite irregular. The best match, if it meets a certain criterion of good fit, is identified by the machine as the word just spoken; otherwise the machine declares a non-match.

36

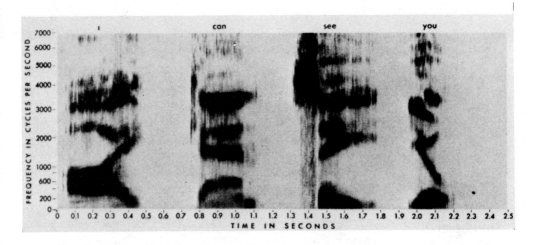

Figure 3-1. Speech spectrogram of a sentence. The darker the image, the greater the momentary sound level at the corresponding frequency. Automatic speech recognizers work with digitized versions of such "visible speech." (From Peter B. Denes and Elliot N. Pinson, *The Speech Chain.* Murray Hill, New Jersey: Bell Telephone Laboratories, Inc., 1963. Used with permission.)

Kinds of Recognizers

Commercially available speech recognizers can be classified on two key dimensions: whether they are speaker-independent or speaker-dependent and whether they recognize discrete speech or connected speech.

Machines that are speaker-independent are designed to be trained for any particular utterance in the voices of several speakers, perhaps five to ten of them. The word reference information stored away for any utterance to be recognized then compensates for the variations in the way different people may say the same word. Such word recognizers are reasonably successful at recognizing the speech of someone not previously providing a speech sample. There is a trade-off penalty for speaker-independent recognition, however. The amount of computer memory required for word reference pattern information is much greater, allowing an active vocabulary perhaps only one-tenth of the size possible when recognition is confined to one particular speaker.

Speaker-independent machines can recognize many speakers, but at a cost.

37

Discrete speech recognition is recognition one-word-at-a-time as opposed to speech as it flows naturally without deliberate pauses between words. The typical discrete-speech recognizer requires that the speaker pause at least one-tenth of a second between words. With a *connected*-speech recognizer, the speaker need not introduce a deliberate pause between words but can speak in a more or less natural flow. Devices offering connected-speech recognition tend also to be speaker-dependent—the combined challenge of connected and speaker-independent recognition is most formidable.

Connected speech does not mean *continuous* speech. A connected-speech recognizer looks for a break or pause in the flow of speech and then proceeds to analyze the last several seconds of speech heard. Present-day machines cannot keep pace with a rapid, continuous talker.

There's a difference between connected speech and continuous speech.

A key difficulty associated with the recognition of connected speech is that the speech signal for any particular word is influenced by the words that go before and after it (the problem of *coarticulation*).[3] Thus the beginnings and ends of words in the speech stream lack the relatively "clean" boundaries they would have if spoken in isolation. This feature complicates matching incoming words with the stored word reference patterns—the previously "trained" vocabulary items—since each of those words was spoken individually.

How Well Do Recognizers Work?

How well do automatic speech recognizers recognize speech? Test results furnished by the vendors of recognition systems, as we might expect, reflect impressive levels—for example, 99.4 percent "correct recognition." Such test results, however, reflect optimal conditions, including low ambient noise, trained and confident speakers, and selected vocabularies.

Subjective factors can play a big role in the human user producing speech that can readily be recognized by machine. The confidence with which the speaker addresses the machine is apparently such a factor.[4] If you *expect* your speech to be recognized correctly, the machine's performance tends to be correspondingly better.

Also enhancing recognition performance are vocabularies with high information content (vocabularies of words that are phonetically distinct and thus less apt to be confused with one another). With vocabularies that are not especially selected from highly dissimilar words, recognition performance, other things being equal, will fall off. The phrase "other things being equal," by the way, labels a key problem in evaluating the performance of speech recognizers. A lack of standard procedures for evaluation has made meaningful statements about recognition performance, especially comparisons between machines, difficult if not impossible.[5]

Humans as Speech Recognizers

How well do *people* recognize speech, especially when there are less than optimal conditions? The classic study of the intelligibility of speech to humans as a function of the context in which that speech is heard was performed over thirty years ago by psychologist George A. Miller and his associates at Harvard University's psychoacoustics laboratory.[6] They presented speech samples to listeners under varying levels of *white noise,* a neutral audio background consisting of a random mix of sound energies across the audible spectrum. In one part of their study, they presented "target" words either in isolation or as part of a meaningful sentence. In another part of their study, one-syllable words were used, while the *size* of the test vocabulary was systematically varied from 2, 4, 8, 16, 32, to 256 words.

The overall finding was that it is not so much the item itself that determines how intelligible it is over varying levels of white noise as it is the *context* in which the item occurs. As we reduce the range of alternative possibilities of what a word may be—by restricting the size of the vocabulary, setting it in a meaningful sentence, or whatever—we thereby enhance the probability of its accurate discrimination. Otherwise performance falls—falls, one is tempted to say, to the level of performance of automatic speech recognizers that operate without contextual cues.

The intelligibility of speech depends above all on context.

SPEECH AND CONTEXT

Automatic speech recognizers are usually required to perform under what we would call, for humans, conditions of sensory deprivation. For people to perform under such conditions, they would have to be put into isolation tanks, out of touch, sight, and, except for the test material, out of sound.

Although the origins of speech are obscure and may never be uncovered by scholars,[7] speech surely developed originally between people who could see one another and also the world that was the subject of their talk. Gesture and looking about must have accompanied the chatter. The essential role of *setting* in the recognition of speech tends somehow to be forgotten when speech recognition (by humans or machine) enters the laboratory. It helps in the recognition of speech if you have some inkling, from common context, of what someone is apt to be saying.

From the setting comes recognition.

I recall encountering, while on a noontime walk near MIT's Cambridge campus, a family at curbside, roadmaps spread over their car roof. A woman, ostensibly the mother, hailed me for help. She spoke no English and simply uttered, over and over, a word I could not make out. Suddenly, somehow combining her hand-pointing with the sound she made, I realized that she was trying to say "Lechmere" (pronounced locally as "Leech-meer," accent on the first syllable), a section of Cambridge. What was a moment before simply noise became *heard* as "Lechmere-with-an-accent." Through more gestures and words, I was able to get the family headed on its way.

Speech is where we speak it.

Much of speech is, literally, where we *speak* it. What we see about us shapes what we do and say as well as how we interpret things. Imagine you are standing with an acquaintance at courtside, both of you in tennis clothes and carrying tennis gear. Automatically, you both are set for light conversation concerning how your respective games are going, whom you played recently, and forth. Your talk is apt to be much different when meeting this same person at the office, both of you in business garb, with briefcases and sheaves of reports. Even the casual remark "How's the racquet going?"—the pun is intentional—is heard differently.

The point is this: Our surroundings can operate as a constraint upon speech by influencing what is said in the first place and also how it's heard. In automatic speech recognition, constraining what the user may say—by sharpening the question to narrow the range of plausible responses, for example—has been shown to make user/system dialogue more robust.[8] A promising, yet largely unexplored, role for graphic imagery at the user/system interface concerns its use as a constraint on what the user may say or do. Imagery can define the situation for the user, so that the user speaks and acts in light what is "out there." In turn, this context of graphic images can help the user understand what the system is doing, even aid the user in interpreting mechanical speech.

40

WHEN GESTURE IS GESTURE

Cautioning against attributing to every act deep psychosexual under-
tones, Sigmund Freud is reputed to have remarked that "sometimes
a cigar is just a cigar."

How do we know that a certain wave of the hand is indeed a
gesture and not simply a hand waving idly in the air with no relevant
intention behind it? Certain hand movements—or eyeblinks, shoul-
der shrugs, or whatever—*attain* to gesture in the eye of the beholder
by virtue of the context in which they are employed. They are
perceived as gesture because of the observer's cognizance of that
context.

The meaning of gesture, too, depends on the context.

Imagine sitting in our Media Room chair and pointing at the
large screen. Suppose the computer is trying to make sense of your
gesture. How high and away from the body you hold your hand is of
importance. If you're holding it low and close to your body, it is
probably not a pointing gesture; held out and away, it well may be.
Interpretation further depends on what you are pointing at, as well as
on what you are or are not saying.

How close you hold your hand to the screen can be a useful cue
as well. The act of pointing has, in effect, a *cone of indication* ema-
nating from it. (See Figure 3-2.) The farther your hand is from any
plausible referent, the wider the base of the cone. You may be
referring to an entire region or to something within that region. As
you bring your hand closer, the base of the cone of indication becomes smaller, sharpening the reference (Figure 3-2a). Thus if you
say "That one" while your hand is still far from the screen, the
indication is ambiguous. Bring your hand nearer, however, and your
intention becomes sharper. (In fact, the amount of information in
bits—the *utility* in an information-theory sense—of the exertion of
moving nearer the screen while pointing can in principle be calcu-
lated.) Conversely, we can be too close to things to indicate them
with a relatively static pointing. In this case the solution may be not to
move back but rather to become dynamic in our pointing as in Figure
3-2b.

The "cone of indication" defines our intention.

CAPTURING SPEECH IN THE MEDIA ROOM

As of this writing, speech recognition in our laboratory's Media Room
is by a DP-200 Connected-Speech Recognition System developed

41

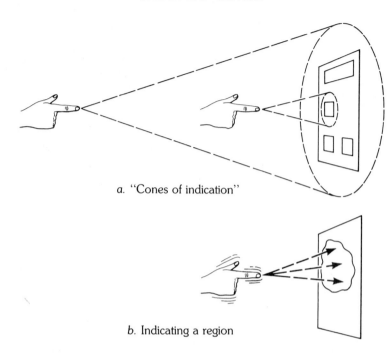

a. "Cones of indication"

b. Indicating a region

Figure 3-2. Patterns of pointing. *(a)* An implicit "cone of indication" emanates from the finger. The base of this cone is relatively large when the hand is some distance from the screen, becoming smaller as the hand is brought closer. *(b)* Wagging the hand serves to indicate a wider region.

The NEC system captures connected speech.

by Nippon Electric Company (NEC) America (Figure 3-3). No pause between words is necessary when speaking to it, and up to five words or "utterances" are permitted per spoken sentence.[9] A key achievement of the NEC system is getting around the *segmentation problem*—determining where any word in a continuous stream of speech starts and stops—by techniques of dynamic programming and dual-level matching on both the individual word level and the level of the entire input utterance.

The recognition response time at the end of each sentence spoken to it is about 300 milliseconds. The text of the utterance is presented on an LED alphanumeric display, and codes representing the recognized words may be sent to a computer connected to the DP-200.

The device's vocabulary, held in the recognizer's active memory

Figure 3-3. The Nippon Electric Company (NEC) connected speech recognizer, model DP-200. The only part in contact with the user is the lightweight combination microphone/headphone at the far right. (Photo courtesy of NEC America, Inc.)

as a set of word reference patterns, comprises a maximum of 120 words. Except for the digits 1 to 10, which must be spoken twice by the user when training the machine, each word in training mode need be spoken only once. The standard system comes with a lightweight, head-mounted microphone.

CAPTURING GESTURE IN THE MEDIA ROOM

The TV monitors in our Media Room are equipped with touch-sensitive screens, but what about pointing at things on the large screen? A space position and orientation sensing technology suitable for our intentions has been developed by Polhemus Navigation Sciences, Inc.[10] This system, called ROPAMS (remote object position attitude measurement system), works essentially as follows.

The ROPAMS system captures gesture.

Two plastic cubes are involved (Figure 3-4, *see* Color Insert). The larger of the two, about 1¼ inches on edge, called the *transmitter,* is mounted on a lucite pedestal near the user's chair. The transmitter is connected by cable underneath the Media Room floor to the ROPAMS-dedicated computer across the lab in our machine room. The transmitter cube works in conjunction with the smaller cube, about ¾ inch on edge, attached to the Media Room end of the

43

ROPAMS system cabling by a length of lightweight cord. This smaller cube, called the *sensor,* is what is tracked in space.

Electric coils in the cubes create magnetic fields surrounding either cube. Then, provided the sensor cube is within about 4 feet of the stationary transmitter cube, the spatial relationship between the two cubes can be determined from the interaction of their magnetic fields. The system can deliver, about ten times per second, the *position* in space (*xyz* spatial coordinates) and *attitude* in space (which way it's tipped) of the little cube relative to the big cube. Fixing the big cube in a known spot in the room then lets the system readily determine where in the room the little cube is and how it's tipped— that is, where it's pointing.

With this description of our lab's speech and space technologies, let us turn to a practical example of how they may be used in concert.

"PUT-THAT-THERE"

"Put-That-There" is the nickname given our prototype speech-and-gesture experiment.[11] Suppose you are seated before the Media Room's large screen. The space-sensing cube is attached to a watch-band on your wrist; the recognition system's microphone is ready and listening. Now let us see some of the commands you may invoke.

"Create . . ."

In our demonstration system, the large screen is initially clear or bears some simple backdrop such as a map. Against this background, items are called into existence, moved about, replicated, their attributes altered, and then they may be ordered to vanish. Some of the items used are basic shapes: circles, squares, diamonds.

The Create command produces basic shapes on the screen.

They are nonrepresentational in that the thing is the shape. They have variable attributes: *color* (red, yellow, orange, green, blue, . . .) and *size* (large, medium, small).

The user points to some spot on the blank screen. A small, white "x" on the screen, the cursor, provides visual feedback for pointing. The user then says: "Create a blue square . . . there." Since the user doesn't indicate the size of the square, the default size, medium, is used. A blue square appears, centered on the spot where the user

44

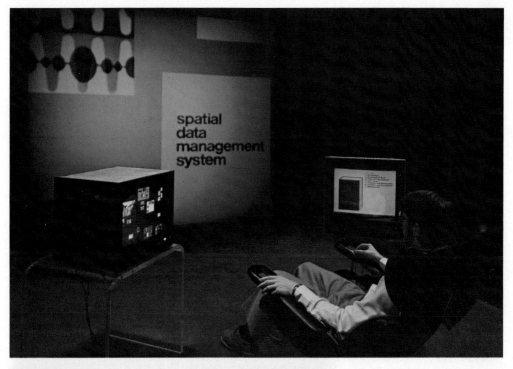

Figure 2-3. The Media Room in use with the spatial data-management system.

Figure 2-4. MIT's Dataland. Note the translucent "you-are-here" marker towards the lower left of the screen.

Figure 2-11. Accessing the "telephone" in Dataland. (See the upper-left quadrant of Figure 2-13 for the telephone touch-control image.)

Figure 2-13. Keymaps for controlling data types in Dataland: telephone (upper left); calculator (upper right); book (lower left); TV (lower right). These images come up (separately) on the keymap monitor when the corresponding item is zoomed-in on in Dataland.

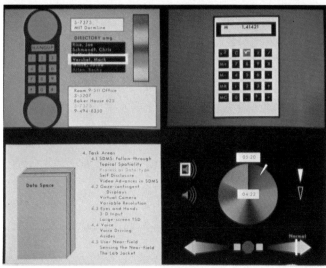

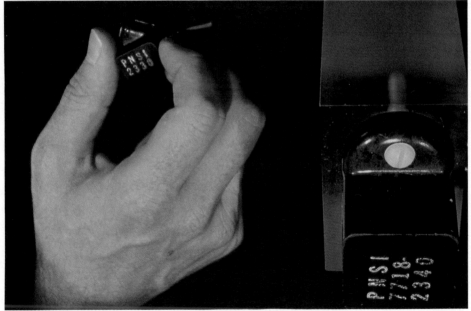

Figure 2-18. The CCA spatial data-management aboard the USS Carl Vinson.

Figure 3-4. The ROPAMS space-sensing cubes: the transmitter cube (left) and the sensor cube.

Figure 3-7. Put-That-There. Deploying ships about the Caribbean Sea via speech and pointing. The items being manipulated here are circle and diamond shapes standing for ships or small fleets being moved about against the backdrop of a Caribbean map. The user is wearing a lightweight head microphone. Strapped to the user's arm—here caught in a double exposure effect—is the smaller of the pair of space-sensing cubes (covered by the user's cuff). On a pedestal to the user's right is a lucite block on top of which is the larger of the pair of space-sensing cubes. (Photo copyright 1980, Association for Computing Machinery, Inc. Used with permission.)

Figure 4-5. The "World of Windows". Up to thirty images are on display at one time. This is how the world of windows appears to the user seated before the Media Room's large screen. The majority of the windows are dynamic with sound, representing ongoing, real-world events. They are presumed assembled by an information-gathering network for display to the user—in this context supposed to be a high-level decision maker. Looking at any one episode will first cause the soundtracks of all other episodes to turn off. Further looking at that episode will cause a "cut" to a full-screen version of the episode. (Photo copyright 1981, Association for Computing Machinery, Inc. Used with permission.)

Figure 5-2. The "Movie Map". Driving by videodisk about the streets of Aspen, Colorado. The view on the top screen is a down-the-street view. A tiny translucent insert map at the top-middle of this screen shows the user's route with respect to Aspen's two main streets. The horizontally mounted monitor provides a top-down view of the street grids of Aspen in the spirit of a conventional map. Again, the user's route is indicated in red on this monitor. Thus the movie map offers something a conventional map cannot, namely the experience of "being there" while preserving the broad orienting features of the conventional map.

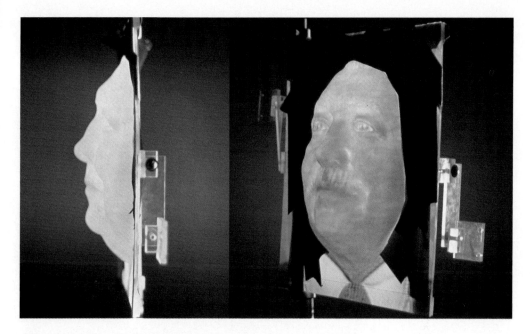

Figure 5-7. The talking-head "persona". Back-projecting a full-color TV facial image upon the translucent face-shaped screen creates a vivid sense of the "presence" of the person. In the teleconferencing situation the TV projection comes from the local videodisk, while the person's speech arrives via telephone lines. Mixed in with the remote speaker's speech signal is head-position information generated by a space-sensing cube worn on the head. The face screen will turn and nod in perfect synchrony with the remote speaker's head gestures. Lip motions are generated locally as a function of the transmitted speech to create a convincing impression. Eye movements may be dubbed in locally in a naturally random way, or could in principle be driven by remote eye tracking.

Technology

Penthouse magazine will launch an adult programming service for pay and cable television next April in

International

From a summit you should be able to see where you're going as well as where you've been. There were at least three encouraging instances of looking ahead at the recent Versailles summit: ★ Technology. The leaders of the seven major industrial

Financial

Rural education officials should return to the virtues of the one-room country school instead of creating "second-rate imitations" of metropolitan schools, a rural education specialist says. "The one-room schoolhouse was a valuable history lesson

Legal & Political

President Reagan will speak by satellite telecast Friday to job training seminars around the nation

Popular

Satellite Netw Delivery Corp

People

... presidents were Derek B Harvard, Paul MIT, David S University of

... education present will President Pau National Scien Foundation P John Slaughte ... year, said scientist Jero Wiesner critic Nixon's 1969

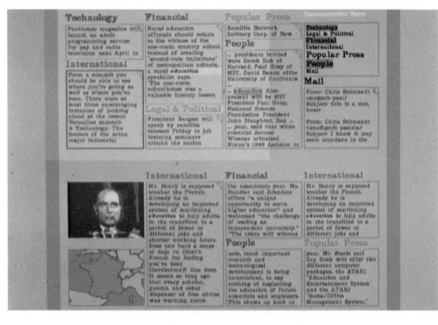

Figure 6-1. Images from MIT's "Communication News" project. The entire news page appears on the monitor (top), with the ability on that monitor to "window" in closer upon that image (bottom). With the close-in image (bottom), the news sheet can be "slid" about under the window via finger pushes on the monitor's touch-sensitive screen. (Images courtesy of Walter Bender.)

is pointing. There is no default color; some color from the preprogrammed ensemble of color names must be given.[12] The same is true for shape.

The feedback cursor's location on the screen at the time the word "there" is spoken becomes the spot where the item will be placed. The spoken "there" is thus functionally a "when"—that is, it serves as a "voice button" for the xy cursor action of the pointing gesture (Figure 3-5).

"Move . . ."

The user can readily move items about the screen. Consider this user command: "Move the blue triangle to the right of the green square." This command relies on voice mode only. Should there exist only one triangle on the screen at the time the command is

The Move command shifts the shapes.

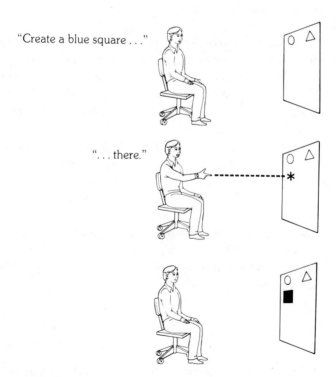

"Create a blue square . . ."

". . . there."

Figure 3-5. Put-That-There. Creating a blue square on the display.

given, the adjective "blue" could well be omitted as it bears no information; the same logic applies to the qualifier "green" in the phrase "green square."

As a result of the Move command the blue triangle, upon "hearing" its name, blinks as immediate feedback that it has been addressed, disappears from its present site, and reappears centered in a spot to the right of the green square.

The exact positioning "to the right" is programmer-determined in our version; some reasonable placement is executed. The interpretation of such relational expressions in graphic space is a complex issue.[13] The important thing is that the item is now where the user has ordered it to be. Minor modifications in position can be made later—for instance, "Move it three inches to the right."

In our example, the user might equally well have said: "Move *that* to the right of the green square." In this option, the user employs the pronoun *that* while simultaneously pointing to the item that should be moved. The word *that*—plus the act of pointing—is functionally equivalent to the speech string " . . . the blue triangle . . ."[14]

A pronoun plus pointing defines the item.

Further, the target spot can be rendered simply by *there*, as in "Put that . . . *there.*" *There,* now indicated by gesture, serves in lieu of the entire phrase "to the right of the green square." This ability to indicate place by saying "there" and pointing is especially useful when in fact no reference item yet exists near the spot where you want to create or move an item.

In this function, as in others, some variation in expression is understandably a valuable option. Thus a mini-thesaurus of common synonyms, such as *move, put, place,* and the like, is built into the vocabulary, as well as a capability to declare a synonym for any vocabulary item.

Further, the user can invoke a special Designate command, saying, for example: "Designate 'transfer' . . . 'move.'" This command adds the utterance *transfer* to the vocabulary, making its effect the same as saying "move."

"Copy . . ."

The Copy command is simply a variant of the Move command, in that the image of the item to be moved also remains in place at its original spot (Figure 3-6).

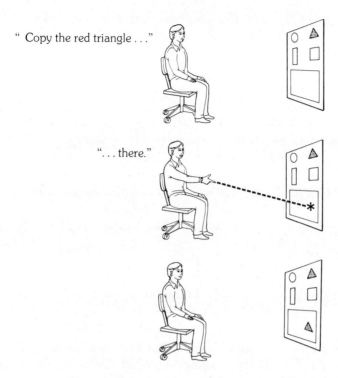

" Copy the red triangle . . ."

". . . there."

Figure 3-6. Put-That-There. The Copy command leaves the original item in place, with an identical figure appearing where indicated.

"Make . . ."

The main attributes of any item the user has called into existence can be modified. In our system the main attributes are color, size, and shape. For example, the utterance "Make the blue triangle small" causes the referenced item to become reduced in size. Reference in this case is by voice alone. The user could instead have said, pointing to the desired item, "Make *that* smaller." The command "Make that a large blue diamond," uttered while the user points at a small yellow circle, causes the indicated changes in the figure.

Extrapolations readily suggest themselves—for example, the command "Make that (indicating some item) like that (indicating some other item)." The item indicated when the second "that" is uttered becomes the model for change. The action on the screen is

The Make command alters size, color, and shape.

an expunging of the first referenced item, to be replaced in a Copy-like fashion by the second referenced item.

"Delete . . ."

The Delete command erases single items or the entire screen.

The Delete command (synonyms: Erase; Expunge; Take out) allows the user to drop certain items from display. As before, the operand of the command can be "the large blue circle" or "that" (pointing to some item). Again, variations and extrapolations of the basic notion suggest themselves: global expunging, "clear" or "delete everything," in order to wipe the graphic slate clean; or, perhaps, "Delete everything to the left of this (drawing a line vertically down the face of the screen)."

"Call . . ."

The Call command links a sound pattern to the item.

Suppose the user points to a certain item on display and says "Call that . . . the calendar." This command causes the sound pattern "the calendar" to become directly linked in the data base to whichever item the user chooses, by pointing, to call "the calendar."

Alternatively, the user could have said, without an accompanying pointing gesture, "Call the item . . . in the top left corner . . . the calendar." Provided there is only one item in the top left corner—so that the reference is unambiguous—the pointing is done by a set of words that uniquely designates the item.

The system is indifferent to the sound pattern that is attached to the item. The policy on naming is as pragmatic as the supposed origin in the English language of the word *kangaroo*. Early English explorers in Australia inquired of aborigines via gesture what that strange, long-tailed, high-jumping creature was called. Purportedly the aborigines pointed to it and replied "Kan ga-roo," aborigine for "I don't know."

All of these commands concern themselves with the simple management of a limited ensemble of nonrepresentative objects. They are intended to suggest the versatility and ease of use that characterize the management of graphic space when voice and gesture are used in concert. Further examples of commanding things in a meaningful space come to mind—like moving ships about sea lanes in the Caribbean (Figure 3-7, *see* Color Insert).

ECONOMY IN CONVERSATION

"Put-That-There" uses syntactic and situational cues when interpreting spoken input.[15] In the context of a Caribbean Sea and ship situation, for example, consider the command "Copy the green freighter . . . southwest of the Dominican Republic." Suppose the system interprets the first part of the incoming sound pattern as "* the green freighter," where the asterisk signifies a word not matching any stored pattern meeting a certain criterion of good fit. Valid words in that position could be, for example, *move, replicate, delete,* and the like. From syntactic considerations the missing word must be a *command.* Having inferred this, the system then asks the user via a synthesized-speech voice: "What command?" Because the user usually responds with a single word—in this instance "Copy"—the repeated bit of speech is highly likely to be properly recognized as it is being spoken in isolation, free from acoustic "contamination" from coarticulation with words coming before or after.

This system picks up cues from context and syntax.

Or suppose there had been several freighters of various colors about on the Caribbean map and the user simply starts off with "Copy the freighter. . . ." The user neglects to specify which freighter by color and doesn't point out any specific one. The system doesn't say "Please repeat" but asks "Which freighter?", to which the user may reply "The green one" or "That one (pointing)."

Thus the user is not required mindlessly to repeat entire phrases when only some part was missed (or was missing). This style of interaction does more than conserve information and the user's effort. It reinforces in the user the important feeling that the system is making an intelligent effort to understand and interpret what is being said. This perception can go a long way to enhance the user's acceptance of a system that is bound to make occasional errors.

There's no need to repeat entire phrases.

HIGHLIGHTS

- Approaches to automatic speech recognition that rely on signal processing techniques may well have reached the point of diminishing returns.
- Concurrent information in other modes—such as pointing and gesture—can amplify and clarify what is said. Conversely, speech can clarify and give meaning to gestures.

- The essence of the "Put-That-There" exercise is the ability to substitute a pronoun plus pointing for a longer string of words.
- Much of speech is where we speak it. Computer graphics can supply that sense of "whereness"—both to lend a setting to the user's speech productions and to aid the system's comprehension.

NOTES

[1.] S. E. Levinson and M. Y. Liberman, "Speech Recognition by Computer," *Scientific American* 244(4)(April 1981):64–76.

[2.] This chapter is not meant to be a comprehensive introduction to automatic speech recognition concepts or technologies. Useful introductions to the subject include the Levinson and Liberman article (see note 1) as well as M. Elphick, "Unravelling the Mysteries of Speech Recognition," *High Technology* 2(2)(March/April 1982):71–78. The issue devoted to "Man-Machine Communication by Voice," *Proceedings of the IEEE* 64(4)(April 1976), includes articles for both the uninitiated and the more advanced reader. See also Wayne A. Lea (ed.), *Recent Trends in Automatic Speech Recognition* (Englewood Cliffs, N.J.: Prentice-Hall, 1980).

[3.] See D. R. Reddy, "Speech Recognition by Machine: A Review," *Proceedings of the IEEE* 64(4)(April 1976):501–531, especially pp. 508–511 and 518–519.

[4.] A. L. Robinson, "More People Are Talking to Computers as Speech Recognition Enters the Real World," *Science* 203(16 February 1979):634–638.

[5.] The problem of establishing more systematic and objective performance evaluation is receiving attention. The possibility of development and widespread use of uniform performance assessment methodologies and standardized test data bases was the theme of a workshop on Standardization for Speech I/O Technology held at the National Bureau of Standards in Gaithersburg, Maryland, 18–19 March 1982, under the joint sponsorship of the National Bureau of Standards, the Institute for Computer Sciences and Technology (ICST), and the Naval Air Development Center (NADC).

[6.] G. A. Miller, G. A. Heise, and W. Lichten, "The Intelligibility of Speech as a Function of the Context of the Test Material," *Journal of Experimental Psychology* 41(1951):329–335.

7. C. F. Hockett, "The Origins of Speech," *Scientific American* 203(3)(September 1960):89–96.

8. J. L. Flanagan, "Computers That Talk and Listen: Man-Machine Communication by Voice," *Proceedings of the IEEE* 64(4)(April 1976):405–415, especially pp. 412–413.

9. In mid-1982, Nippon Electric Company introduced its model DP-200 Connected Speech Recognizer. This model takes in 4.5 seconds of speech for analysis (as opposed to 2.5 seconds of speech for the earlier DP-100) and breaks down that sample into a maximum of ten words (as opposed to a maximum of five words for the earlier model).

10. Polhemus Navigational Sciences, Inc., P.O. Box 298, Essex Junction, VT 05452. For a technical description, see F. H. Rabb, E. B. Blood, T. O. Steiner, and H. R. Jones, "Magnetic Position and Orientation Tracking System," *IEEE Transactions on Aerospace and Electronic Systems,* AES-15, no. 5, September 1979, pp. 709–718.

11. Richard A. Bolt, "'Put-That-There': Voice and Gesture at the Graphics Interface," *Computer Graphics* 14(3)(1980):262–270. (© 1980, Association for Computing Machinery, Inc. Excerpts and illustrations used with permission.) Systems implementation of the prototype was magnificently executed by Chris Schmandt and Eric Hulteen.

12. Apropos of color, a more ambitious "interpretive" approach might be to match the utterance "green" to pixel values; the matching could be mediated through the classic CIE color space, partitioned into a number of nameable regions. The partitioning of the CIE color space on the basis of an ensemble of color names could be programmer-determined on an ad hoc basis, or the partitioning might involve sophisticated calibration by having subject observers name or classify displayed colors. The essential point is that the mapping from attribute-name to item-attribute can be well defined, even though it may be as complex as one cares to attempt.

13. N. K. Sondheimer, "Spatial Reference and Natural-Language Machine Control," *International Journal of Man-Machine Studies* 8(1976):329–336. See also Patrick Winston, "Learning Structural Descriptions from Examples," MIT Project MAC, TR-76, 1970.

14. "That" is thus defined as whatever is pointed out; effectively, it is "ostensively defined." For the namer, at least, the process is not unlike that of telling a small child what things "are"—pointing at a

cat, for example, and saying "cat" or "kitty." The meaning of the word is given by indicating the intended referent in the context of alternatives—namely, whatever else is in the scene. See D. R. Olson, "Language and Thought: Aspects of a Cognitive Theory of Semantics," *Psychological Review* 77(1970):257–273.

[15.] Specific strategies for improving the *effective* performance of speech recognizers are noted in Christopher Schmandt and Eric Hulteen, "The Intelligent Voice-Interactive Interface," *Proceedings of the Conference on Human Factors in Computer Systems* (New York: Association for Computing Machinery, 1982), pp. 363–366; Christopher Schmandt, "Voice Interaction: Putting Intelligence into the Interface," *Proceedings, Conference on Cybernetics and Society* (Seattle: IEEE, 1982).

4.

Eyes as Output

- *Eye Actions*
- *Tracking Technologies*
- *Dynamic Windows: A Prototype*
- *Processing Where You Look*
- *The Prospects for Tracking*
- *Highlights*

In computer parlance, *output* means data resulting from internal processing. Eyes are output in the sense that their position and movements are the result of the internal information processing that the brain and visual system perform on the visible world about us. Where our eyes are looking, where they are moving, is the result of our moment-to-moment internal processing.

Paying attention to where the eyes are trained via *eyetracking methods* has been done mainly in three areas: in human factors studies for the military, as in observing where fighter pilots look on their cockpit instrument array;[1] in research on reading;[2] and in bioengineering to help the handicapped communicate.[3] For the most part, eyetracking has been a laboratory instrument to measure the position and movement of eyes in response to experimental conditions set up by the investigator. Rarely have eye movements and eye position in their own right been enlisted as part of the essential information that an interactive, computer-based information system must have about what the human user is doing.[4] This use of eyes is the subject of this chapter: *eyes* as "output" from the human to the computer.

EYE ACTIONS

The eye is an excellent pointer.

What kind of *eye* actions might it be useful to observe in the context of the human/computer interface? Certainly the *eye* is a pointer *par excellence*. We can look at things in the visual field directly and steadily, micromovements of the *eye* (*tremor* and *drift*) notwithstanding.[5] We can look at some fine bit of detail in a scene, look away, and then return dead on target—all with exquisite repeatability.[6]

While the *eye* thus serves well as a pointer to something on a display terminal, it is less clear how good the *eye* would be in a dynamic role such as "writing" with the *eye* or perhaps guiding a cursor. Except when tracking a moving object—as when following the tip of a moving finger—the *eye* cannot move smoothly. Instead it jumps from point to point in brisk movements called *saccades*. Even the most practiced of visual skills—reading—proceeds via a series of perhaps four to seven discrete jump-and-fixation steps per printed line.[7] Thus writing-by-eye may not be tenable unless a graphic technique such as *b-splining* permits the regeneration of a smooth, continuous contour from a succession of points.[8]

What about using the eye to, say, guide a graphic paddle to intercept a graphic ping-pong ball and deflect it back? Rather than attempting instantaneous control of the paddle's path, the best strategy may be to use the eye's point of regard to indicate where the paddle should go in order to intercept the ball. This task is rather like programming the movements of a robotic arm in terms of destination points rather than in terms of an explicit path.

TRACKING TECHNOLOGIES

Standard eyetracking is often obtrusive.

Many standard eyetracking methods require that observers be constrained somehow from moving, often by obliging them to hold a "bite-board" clamped in their teeth.[9] This restriction hardly makes for unobtrusive observation of the eyes. At least two methods do away with this requirement, however. The first involves wearing an eyeglass frame; in the second the observer need not wear any special apparatus at all.

54

Eyeglass-Mounted Tracking

The approach known as eyeglass-mounted tracking uses a miniature corneal-reflection tracking system housed within or on conventional eyeglass frames.[10] Figure 4-1 illustrates the glasses. A small light-emitting diode (LED) emits infrared radiation with a wavelength of 0.93 micrometer. There is an infrared or "hot mirror" mounted in the glasses frame in the position normally occupied by a prescription lens. This hot mirror is transparent to all light normally utilized by the eye for vision, but it reflects the infrared light from the LED. The mirror also reduces the infrared light reaching the eye from external sources, so that the total infrared radiation impinging upon the eye is less than that which would normally reach the eye from natural sources.[11]

The mirror is of plane glass, but a regular prescription lens could be coated to produce hot mirror qualities, permitting the glasses to be

Eyetracking can be glasses-mounted.

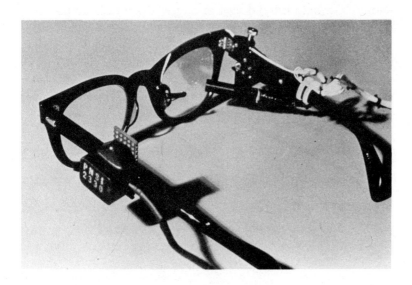

Figure 4-1. Eyeglass-mounted tracking. Here the miniature tracking system is housed in conventional eyeglass frames. The glasses shown, made by Denver Research Institute, measure eye position with respect to the glasses frame. Note the addition of the ROPAMS spacesensing cube on the left bow of the glasses. The cube provides the position of the glasses in a room. The combination of the two measurements gives the wearer's point of regard with respect to the surroundings.

of the corrective type to suit the viewer. The reflected light path is in a *W* shape: from LED to mirror, to cornea, back to mirror, and finally to an image sensor array (Figure 4-2). The image sensor unit is a small tube, ½ inch long and 0.28 inch on the outside diameter, mounted on the bow of the glasses. At one end is a tiny lens that focuses the corneal reflection of the LED onto an image sensor, namely a 32 by 32 photodiode array about 3.8 millimeters on edge.[12] A filter in the tube reduces ambient light that would interfere with eyetracking if it reached the photodiode array.

The corneal reflection, a virtual image of the LED formed about 4 millimeters behind the spherical surface of the cornea, moves about the 32 by 32 element sensor array as the eye rotates in its socket. The glasses unit determines the *xy* position of the LED reflection of the sensor array and outputs it as a ten-bit code at a rate of about twelve coordinate pairs per second.

The glasses themselves track the eye only with respect to the frame of the glasses: about ±15 degrees up and down from center and ±15 degrees left and right of center. The glasses do not track relative to the user's surroundings. To achieve point-of-regard tracking with respect to the surroundings, we have combined the glasses with the space-sensing cubes described earlier. The corneal-reflection tracking embedded in the glasses provides a measure of the eye's orientation within the eyeglass frame, while the space sensor

We combined the eyetracking glasses with space sensors.

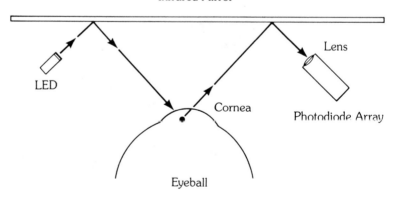

Figure 4-2. Diagram showing the optical path of corneal reflection from light-emitting diode (LED) to sensing photodiode array. (After Rinard and Rugg, 1977.)

attached to the frame provides a measure of the orientation of the glasses with respect to the environment. The two measures combined give the desired point of regard.

The device provides an accuracy of about ±2.5 to ±3.5 degrees. (For the reader's reference, the width of your thumb held out at arm's length represents approximately 2 degrees of arc.) The space-sensing cubes give spatial attitude readings to an accuracy of one-tenth of 1 degree, and thus in their own right they contribute no appreciable error above and beyond the intrinsic accuracy of the glasses. The combined glasses-and-cube provide a serviceable level of resolution, given that one arranges displays not to have key features closer together than the composite device can resolve—although the precision is decidedly less than, say, the tracking system to be described in the next section. While this glasses-mounted system is decidedly not unobtrusive and it lacks fine precision, it does have the advantage of permitting relatively unrestricted head motion as well as unrestricted vertical and horizontal range.

Remote Tracking

Of the eyetracking techniques commercially available, the technique least obtrusive to the observer is the pupil-center/corneal-reflection distance method.[13] This method of tracking measures the fixation point of the observer, the point of regard as it falls on the surroundings, not simply the position of the eye relative to the head. This method is based on two features of the eye that change only with the eye's rotation but not with lateral or vertical displacement: corneal reflection and the center of the pupil. The distance between the two is a direct function of the observer's point of regard.

The least obtrusive eyetracker is the remote-style tracker.

An invisible infrared light source for the corneal reflection is used together with a TV camera sufficiently sensitive in the infrared region to detect this light easily. The TV image, which is zoomed in close to the pupil of the eye, is computer-analyzed; coordinates of the pupil center and of the infrared spot's reflection are determined by timing signals on the video scan.

The infrared spot is not at all obtrusive to the person being monitored, and the small TV set and associated apparatus can be situated about 3 feet from the observer or even farther, depending on the configuration and the use of special lenses.

Applied Science Laboratories, a subsidiary of Gulf and Western

Industries, provides a system of the sort described that allows for extended head motion (see Figures 4-3 and 4-4).[14] The extended head tracking (EHT) unit provides an accuracy of 1 degree or better for a horizontal range of about 40 degrees and a vertical range of about 30 degrees. Coordinates of eye position are provided sixty times per second. Momentary measurements of the user's pupil diameter are provided as well.

Figure 4-3. The G&W Applied Science Laboratories eye-movement monitoring system (Model 1998). The device's optical head—the part that "looks" at the user's eye—is the dark rectangular object mounted horizontally on a pedestal below the large video text display. (The optical head may also be mounted in a vertical orientation.) The cross-hairs on the "eye position" monitor (the small screen on the top left of the computer rack at the left of the picture) show the observer's gaze to be on the seventh line of the displayed text, at about the eleventh character—the "i" in the word *posterity* in an excerpt from the United States Constitution. (Photo courtesy of G&W Applied Science Laboratories, Waltham, Massachusetts.)

58

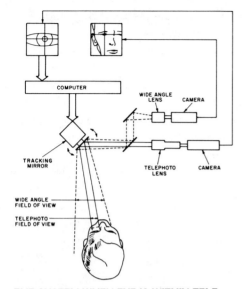 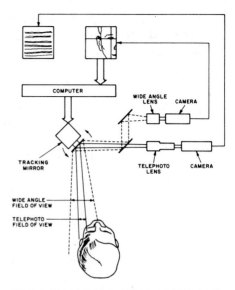

EHT SYSTEM WHEN EYE IS WITHIN TELE-
PHOTO FIELD

EHT SYSTEM WHEN EYE HAS ESCAPED
FROM TELEPHOTO FIELD

Figure 4-4. The extended head-tracking option (EHT) on the G&W Applied Science Laboratories eye view monitor (Model 1998). The extended system uses not only a telephoto image of the observer's pupil but a wide-angle image that includes a much broader field of view of the observer's face. As long as the observer's pupil remains in the small telephoto field, the computer attempts to keep that image centered. If this close-in image of the pupil is lost due to an observer's motion too rapid to follow—e.g., during a sneeze—the computer uses information from the wide-angle view to reacquire the pupil automatically. (Drawings courtesy of G&W Applied Science Laboratories, Waltham, Massachusetts.)

In the following section I'll describe an eye interaction experiment using the eyeglass-mounted style of tracker. While we sorely missed the unobtrusiveness and robustness of the remote-style tracker, that variety of tracking technology was vastly beyond our budget.

DYNAMIC WINDOWS: A PROTOTYPE

The managerial world of the modern executive has been characterized as one of brevity, fragmentation, and variety. Executives spend little time on any one activity. They deal with a great number of

**The modern
executive's
world is
episodic and
highly diverse.**

problems in the course of a day, and the problems they study, and the decisions they make, are of many types.[15]

What might be the display analog of this managerial milieu? One vision of such episodic interaction is that of a large-format display on which upward of twenty—at times perhaps upward of forty—*simultaneous* minidisplays confront the user, the majority of them dynamic and in full color. Such an ensemble would create a salvo of events coming at the executive, events demanding various degrees of attention and decision.

Our goal was to make these ongoing events available to the manager—to post them, as it were—while allowing the manager to focus on any particular one. Our strategy was to let human mechanisms of "selective attention" modulate the display. In the welter of everyday events, the mode *par excellence* of directing attention is vision—specifically, where you are looking.[16]

The World of Windows

At MIT's Architecture Machine Group, we created a five-minute videodisk simulation of what might be coming at a top-level decision-maker in an electronic display system: a veritable World of Windows.[17]

The hypothetical manager would be seated in our Media Room chair about 10 feet back from the 13-foot-diagonal screen. Before the manager would be an array of inset TV images, many more than a person could absorb at one time. Some of the windows would come and go, some appear and persist, others disappear. The precise number of windows on display at any moment would vary, roughly, between fifteen and thirty. (Figure 4-5, *see* Color Insert.)

The *arrangement* of the windows was irregular, though there might be times when a regular grid of windows would be appropriate. The *size* of any window might be used to reflect the density of information in the window and perhaps the importance of its content. We, however, built no "structure" into our prototype World of Windows. That is, the subject matter of a window bore no particular relationship to that window's size or its location relative to neighboring windows. We did do some grouping, however. We lined up three TV news programs at bottom center screen and put four remote hall-monitor TV views, grouped as a 2 by 2 array, in the upper left-hand corner.

Clearly, much more could be attempted in the behind-the-scenes arrangement of the windows, their grouping, layout, size, appearance on color-coded backgrounds, and so forth. Implicit in such a display in actual operation is some kind of information-gathering network: deciding what is to be gathered, gathering it, placing it in certain spots on the large display screen according to some protocol, with or without alerting messages to the observer, and so on. Our simulation presupposes some such supportive network, but our interest was with the observer's interaction with the immediate interface as such, not with a larger supportive context.

Behind the display is an information-gathering network.

Our videodisk simulation included diverse dimensions in its "real-world" timestream of simultaneous ongoing events:

- Conversations
- Groups of people
- Large-scale events (battle maneuvers, for instance, and sports events)
- Newscasts
- Dynamic graphics
- Radar maps

A few interspersed windows were of nonreal-time events: movies and slides, for example.

The videodisk material was intended to simulate a welter of live, real-time, remote channels into ongoing events. Three disks, labeled A, B, and C respectively, were made. All three bore identical five-minute sections consisting of TV frames depicting the collection of windows, each window at small scale in its particular spot. The approximately seventy-three minutes of material—if the TV episodes corresponding to each window were to be strung out temporally one after the other—were distributed about disks A, B, and C at *full-frame* size, about one-third of the material on each disk.

The tiny windows are channels into ongoing events.

The reason for the full-size version of *every* episode was to enable the observer to zoom in upon any episode being looked at and see it at full screen size. The reason for the *three* disks was, as we will see shortly, to enable certain visual effects for freezing and zooming-in on a selected episode.

Filtering Information by Eye

The observer's interaction with the World of Windows proceeded as follows. Initially the sound tracks of all the visible episodes would be heard at once—a cocktail-party mélange of sounds. The observer, wearing the glasses-mounted tracker described above, would be looking about the ensemble of windows.

The eye drives the entire process.

If the eye lingered on any one window—pretimed for several seconds—a first order of *auditory* zooming-in would be triggered. All the sound tracks except the one associated with this episode would be turned off. Additionally, the little window being looked at would become bordered with a broad white stripe.

Should the observer persist in gazing at this same episode, a second order of zooming-in would occur: The small-scale episode would freeze-frame for a moment, followed by a cut to the full-screen version of the episode.

Hence the need, stated above, for a *three*-disk system. One disk is needed to exhibit the set of dynamic windows while briefly "matting through" from the second disk a freeze-frame of the eye-selected episode. The third disk is therefore left free to get into position to play the selected episode at full-screen scale.

Now, alternative ways of zooming-in could be considered. Instead of pretiming the duration of looking, the system could be programmed to respond as well to a deliberate button or lever. This mode might be preferable when speed of entry is essential. Zooming-out—returning from the full-screen episode to the collection of little windows—would be controlled by pulling back on a joystick mounted in the arm of the chair.

PROCESSING WHERE YOU LOOK

Computing or communications resources can be allocated on the basis of where the observer's visual attention is directed. Consider, in a computer network, the progressive transmission of pictures. The general method involves transmitting an image as a sequence of approximations, each approximation having twice the resolution of its predecessor. The first approximation is a monochrome rectangle; the final one is a fully resolved image.[18]

An interesting variation on this theme is nonuniform development—that is, a small region of the image is developed to full resolution before the rest of the image.[19] With eyetracking present, the image could be made to develop first (or only) where the observer is looking. (See Figure 4-6.) The direction of looking could be intentional on the observer's part, or it could be quite incidental to the general act of observing. It all depends on the material being viewed

Imagine "telebrowsing" a whole library of images.

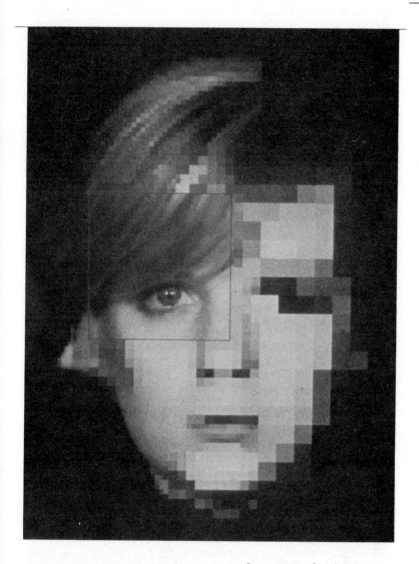

Figure 4-6. Selective development in the progressive transmission of pictures. The image develops first where the observer is looking. (Photo © Scott Fisher/Steve Gano, 1982.)

and the observer's frame of mind. This scenario invites speculation on a kind of gaze-directed low-bandwidth video, or perhaps the "telebrowsing" of a library of images.[20]

THE PROSPECTS FOR TRACKING

Eyetracking at the interface is still an unrealized potential. Beyond the realization of how information about the user's looking behavior could be applied are two crucial issues: cost and convenience.

The Economics of Tracking

The cost of these systems is linked to demand.

The comfortable, unobtrusive tracking systems, essentially those based on remote corneal-reflection methods, are expensive—on the order of $100,000. Their current cost alone prohibits their being considered seriously as potential system components.

Part of the problem of cost stems from the classic chicken-and-egg dilemma. Such unobtrusive systems are currently sold one at a time to research labs as measurement tools, not in quantities as part of what the well-equipped computer interface ought to have in its own right. A growing demand and consequent volume production would help to lower costs. The demand, however, is not there. That eyetracking can become a system component, and not just a laboratory measuring instrument, has not yet really struck home. There is a vague sense that tracking *may* be useful, but no real conviction.

This situation can change. New developments in digitizing camera technology, in tracking-mirror driving, in microprocessors, will make it possible for trackers to be embedded in the terminal as an integral part, eventually at far less cost. As miniaturization and compactness evolve, tracking will become integrated into tabletop terminals and computers. On the utilization front, imaginative uses for tracking will develop—encouraged in part by instrumentation developments, in part perhaps by books like this one. In the long run, the price of a terminal or personal computer will less and less reflect the memory and processing elements, which will become dirt cheap. Rather the price will come to reflect the costs of the electromechanical accoutrements—touch-screens, gesture sensors, and built-in eyetrackers—that capture the user's intentions.

Ease of Use

Beyond the sheer creature comfort the user derives from being tracked at a distance, at least two aspects of remote eyetracking can be pinpointed for improvement: acquisition and calibration.

Acquisition of the eye—or reacquisition should the tracker lose it due to a sudden motion such as a sneeze—needs more attention. The acquisition/reacquisition problem has not been urgently addressed because of the present operating context of eyetracking: the laboratory, where a "human operator" (the experimenter) is assumed to be on the scene to adjust things.

Various schemes have been proposed for automatic eye acquisition. Some involve apparatus placed upon the observer: a light-emitting diode (LED) or magnetic space sensor (like the one I described in Chapter 3) mounted on a headband. Once the observer's general head position is known from sighting the LED or interrogating the space-sensor cube, search algorithms would be invoked to locate the eye socket. Other schemes do not involve items attached to the person being tracked. These include analyzing a wide-angle image of the user's head to search for the "hot spot" reflection off the retina. (This is the "red eye" effect we often observe in flashbulb photos of dogs and cats.)[21] Perhaps thermographic techniques could be used to locate the eye socket in a heat image of the user's head. Or perhaps differential reflectance of the various areas of skin on the face may help—the eyelids are of different skin texture than the rest of the face, for example.

Some of these techniques, or yet new schemes not noted here, may someday produce a tracker that "pounces" upon the eye when you come into its presence—immediately to establish eye contact, even if only one-way contact from you to it—and pounces back upon the eye should it become lost.

The other area that calls for significant improvement in ease of use is that of *calibration*. Even if the human operator of a tracker is somehow supersmooth, the demand that one spend a few minutes at first calibrating it represents a perpetual nuisance. An initial few moments of calibrating is necessary for anyone; our corneas, our spectacles or contact lenses, differ. Beyond that, the need is for "smart," unobtrusive calibration to keep things tuned. If the system found the user consistently looking off-center when interacting with graphic items, for example, perhaps it could silently recalibrate itself

> *More work must be done on acquisition and calibration.*

to compensate for that systematic error. That is, the system would treat the error as real and not just an arbitrary whim of the observer.

HIGHLIGHTS

- Because the eye functions as an excellent pointer, information about our point of regard can be used to modulate the display at the systems interface.
- Eye action can be captured by eyetracking devices: either eye-glass-mounted apparatus or remote-style trackers. Glasses-mounted trackers are serviceable but obtrusive; remote trackers are unobtrusive but costly.
- Our experiment, the World of Windows, demonstrates that an observer can orchestrate a complex display of images by eye action.
- The well-equipped computer interface of the future will have built-in eyetracking—working in concert with speech and gesture recognition—to convey the user's intentions.

NOTES

[1] See Randall L. Harris, Sr., and David M. Christhilf, "What Do Pilots See in Displays?" *Proceedings of the Human Factors Society* (Santa Monica: Human Factors Society, 1980).

[2] See Richard A. Monty and John W. Senders (eds.), *Eyemovements and Psychological Processes* (Hillsdale, N.J.: Erlbaum Associates, 1976). See also John W. Senders, Dennis F. Fisher, and Richard A. Monty (eds.), *Eyemovements and Higher Psychological Processes* (Hillsdale, N.J.: Erlbaum Associates, 1978).

[3] G. A. Rinard and D. E. Rugg, "Current State of Development and Testing of an Ocular Control Device," paper presented at the 1977 Conference on Systems and Devices for the Disabled, Seattle, June 1977. See also, by the same authors, "An Ocular Control Device for Use by the Severely Handicapped," paper presented at the 1976 Conference on Systems and Devices for the Disabled, Boston, June 1976.

[4] The work in note 3 is an instance. See also George W. McConkie,

"The Use of Eye-Movement Data in Determining the Perceptual Span in Reading," in Monty and Senders, *Eye Movements and Psychological Processes.*

5. G. D. Cumming, "Eyemovements and Visual Perception," in E. C. Carterette and M. P. Friedman (eds.), *Handbook of Perception,* Vol. 9: *Perceptual Processing.* New York: Academic Press, 1978.

6. R. Steinman, "Role of Eyemovements in Maintaining a Phenomenally Clear and Stable World," in Monty and Senders, *Eye Movements and Psychological Processes.* We may note that, except for visual reference to something in the surroundings being perceived relative to the fovea or center of vision, the eye's feedback to the observer regarding the point of gaze is quite poor. People generally cannot tell where their own closed eyes are pointing. See Jüri Allick, Marika Rauk, and Aavo Luuk, "Control and Sense of Eye Movement Behind Closed Lids," *Perception* 10(1981):39–51.

7. Keith Rayner, "Eye Movements in Reading and Information Processing," *Psychological Bulletin* 85(3)(1978):618–660.

8. *B-splining* is a computer-graphics technique whereby a continuous smooth curve may be encoded into a series of points. Conversely, a series of points may be used to regenerate (or generate) a continuous curve. See C. DeBoor, *A Practical Guide to Splines,* vol. 27 of *Applied Mathematical Sciences* (New York: Springer-Verlag, 1978).

9. Laurence R. Young and David Sheena, "Survey of Eyemovement Recording Methods," *Behavior Research Methods and Instrumentation* 7(5)(1975):397–429.

10. These tracking glasses are described by Rinard and Rugg, "Current State." The glasses are available from the Denver Research Institute, University of Denver, University Park, Denver, CO 80208.

11. Rinard and Rugg, "An Ocular Control Device," p. 77.

12. The technology for such solid-state imaging devices is discussed in, for example, Steve Ciarcia, "Build the Micro D-Cam Solid State Video Camera," *BYTE* 8(9)(September 1983):20–31.

13. Young and Sheena, "Survey."

14. This unit is the eye view monitor (EVM) system with extended head-tracking option by G&W Applied Science Laboratories, 335 Bear Hill Road, Waltham, MA 02154. The only comparable tracking system is the Honeywell Occulometer Mark II and Mark III; see Young and Sheena, "Survey." Both the Applied Science Laborato-

ries and the Honeywell units provide pupil diameter information as well as point of regard. Such systems can be quite expensive, $100,000 and up, depending on the features and options that are included.

15. Henry Mintzberg, *The Nature of Managerial Work* (Englewood Cliffs, N.J.: Prentice-Hall, 1980), p. 31.

16. Michael J. Posner and Mary Jo Nissen, "Visual Dominance: An Information Processing Account of Its Origins and Significance," *Psychological Review* 83(2)(1976):157–171.

17. R. A. Bolt, "Gaze-Orchestrated Dynamic Windows," *Computer Graphics* 15(3)(August 1981):109–119. (© 1981, Association for Computing Machinery, Inc. Excerpts and illustrations used with permission.)

18. Ken Knowlton, "Progressive Transmission of Grey-Scale and Binary Pictures by Simple, Efficient, and Loss-Less Encoding Schemes," *Proceedings of the IEEE* 68(7)(1980):885–896.

19. I am indebted to Steve Gano, formerly a graduate student at the Architecture Machine Group, for bringing his work on Knowlton's progressive picture transmission schemes to my attention. The image in Figure 4-5 is from Gano's work.

20. F. S. Hill, Jr., Sheldon Walker, Jr., and Fuwen Gao, "Interactive Image Query System Using Progressive Transmission," *Computer Graphics* 17(3)(July 1983):323–330.

21. Applied Science Laboratories (see note 14) offers these head-tracking features as options on their 1998 series EVM system.

5.

The Terminal as Milieu

- *Virtual Solid Space*
- *Overview and Immersion*
- *The User as Actor*
- *Nonplanar Screens*
- *Highlights*

The Media Room is an example of how the terminal can be a *place,* not simply a tiny screen the user perches in front of. It offers extensive visual space and provides, via special sensors, the opportunity for expression by voice, hand, and eye. In this chapter, I return to the notion of the terminal as a rich and varied milieu for human action and involvement.

VIRTUAL SOLID SPACE

In his book *The Poetics of Space,* French writer and philosopher Gaston Bachelard celebrates the hold on imagination exercised by certain kinds of spaces: secret rooms, vast halls, the interiors of sea-shells, the vault of the stars.[1] For me, the spaces *within mirrors* have always held fascination. Along with the "adjoining" rooms created in tiny restaurants by mirrored walls comes the thought of how it would be to enter there, like Alice through the looking glass.

Consider being able to reach into the space behind a mirror and

We can go through the looking glass.

touch and manipulate the images of solid, three-dimensional items. One way to do this was set up by Christopher Schmandt of the Architecture Machine Group at MIT.[2] A color TV set is positioned above a half-silvered mirror at a certain angle so that the observer perceives the face of the TV screen to lie behind and below the mirror's surface (Figure 5-1). If the material on the TV screen is *stereoscopic*, however, the observer sees not a flat TV screen below the mirror but some solid three-dimensional item or items hanging there in space. The observer can then reach in below and behind the mirror to "touch" the items suspended there.

Two separate images of course need to be presented to the observer in order that a stereoscopic image will be seen: one image for the left eye, another, slightly different, for the right. A special technique for presenting *both* stereo picture halves on a single TV monitor exploits the fact that a TV *frame*—the set of horizontal lines painted electronically on the TV screen top-to-bottom every thirtieth of a second—actually consists of two *fields,* one presented after the other. The first field, which consists of the odd-numbered scan lines,

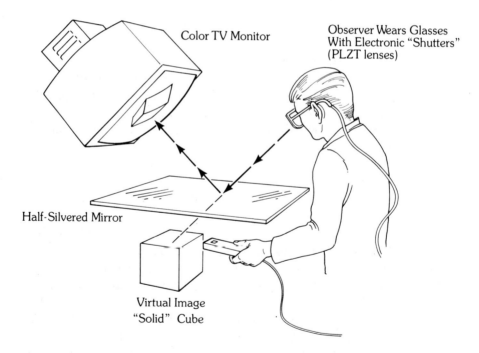

Color TV Monitor

Observer Wears Glasses With Electronic "Shutters" (PLZT lenses)

Half-Silvered Mirror

Virtual Image "Solid" Cube

Figure 5-1. Beyond the looking glass. The solid 3-D image lies behind the half-silvered mirror in a space you can reach into.

holds the left half of the stereo image. The second field consists of the even-numbered scan lines and bears the right half of the stereo image. To ensure that each stereo image half gets presented to the proper eye, the observer wears special glasses with electronic shutters. These shutters open and close in perfect synchrony with the presence on screen of either field of the TV frame.[3]

The observer holds a wand on which is mounted a three-dimensional space-sensing cube, the same cube we use for sensing gestures in the Media Room. The observer can draw in three dimensions with the wand, manipulate images, pick them up, and move them to different spots in the space below the mirror. Although Schmandt did not include them in his version, the addition of speech input and output would effectively create a 3-D version of "Put-That-There" (Chapter 3).

Practical uses for such a 3-D workspace await exploration and exploitation. Applications might include the sculpting of new auto body designs, the solid modeling of oil and gas drilling sites, even— with fine-tuned displays—simulated surgery for medical school classes. (Tactile feedback might become vital in this last instance—a formidable but intriguing challenge.) Such developments aside, there is something about being able to draw in thin air with graphic ink that is just pure fun.

OVERVIEW AND IMMERSION

Imagine yourself on a visit to Hampton Court Palace outside of London, and that you are walking about the famous maze on the palace grounds. The walkway stretches before and behind you, with thick, high shrubbery walls on either side. The route through the maze you have thus far walked is now a *construct* in memory: a mind-picture of the pattern of left/right turns you have made to get where you are.

Now imagine yourself in a helicopter flying above the maze, looking down upon it. You now enjoy a literally superior view. You see directly where you must walk to get out of the maze. Overview thus makes the problem a *perceptual* one, while immersion forces it to remain *conceptual,* whether those concepts are a verbal list of the order of left/right/left turns or an image in the head.[4]

The use of overview on the one hand for general orientation, and the use of immersion on the other for involvement, was seen in

Overviews give us orientation; immersion gives us involvement.

our worldview of Dataland combined with the ability to zoom in on things we wanted to investigate. Another instance of combining overview with immersion is a videodisk-based "Movie Map" of Aspen, Colorado[5] created at the Architecture Machine Group.

Movie footage was taken of travel down all the streets of the town of Aspen, Colorado, one frame per every 9 feet of travel, by a set of truck-mounted cameras. This footage was then transferred to videodisk. With special supporting programs to control image presentation from videodisk, the user can travel about Aspen at street level (Figure 5-2, *see* Color Insert). Left and right turns at any intersection can be made at will by touching left/right arrows graphically overlaid on the touch-sensitive screen of the user's color TV monitor. This surrogate travel about Aspen at street level constitutes an *immersive* point of view.

The Movie Map does not abandon the top-down overview that conventional maps afford. A translucent rectangular overlay appears on the video screen at top and center—about where, taking the video screen as a windshield, your rearview mirror would be. This overlay is a simple map showing Aspen's two main streets as intersecting blue lines, while the track of your route appears in green "ink" as you travel about.

The Movie Map combines overview and immersion.

Moreover, a portion of the videodisk is reserved for full-screen overview maps of the town. There are three styles of map: a street map; streets with buildings and structures (a detail map); and an aerial photo. All three maps are in perfect registration, one with the other, and switchable by touch with the ease of changing TV channels. The user can zoom in on any street intersection by touching it on the monitor. (If desired, the user can go immediately into street-level travel from any intersection so selected.)

The user can indicate travel routes about the town directly on these maps by a series of touches connecting street intersections along the desired path. (See the bottom monitor in Figure 5-2.) Then, upon touching a graphic label Travel, the display switches to dynamic street-level movement along the route just indicated. The user can deviate spontaneously from any such preselected travel path by touching en route the left/right travel control "buttons" on the monitor face.

The Movie Map is a comprehensive alternative to both conventional maps and travelogues. While conventional maps offer an abstract overview of some locale, the Movie Map lets you enter into the environment at street level and move about within it. The conventional travelogue movie offers a visual experience of some place, to be sure, but the story is told from start to finish in the sequence set when the film was edited. In contrast, the Movie Map offers a different agenda every time. The experience is one of direct immersion in vicarious travel: a visit without being there.

An alternative to conventional maps and movie travelogues.

Immersion as such, incidentally, is the specific intent of such supersize screens as those of the IMAX and OMNIMAX motion picture systems.[6] In an IMAX theater, several hundred viewers sit before a rectangular screen that might be as large as 75 by 100 feet. The minimum and maximum viewing angles lie between 60 to 120 degrees horizontally and 40 to 80 degrees vertically for the farthest and nearest viewers respectively. (See Figure 5-3.) In an OMNIMAX theater, the screen is a tilted dome, providing a planetarium-like picture that extends 180 degrees laterally and 20 degrees below and 110

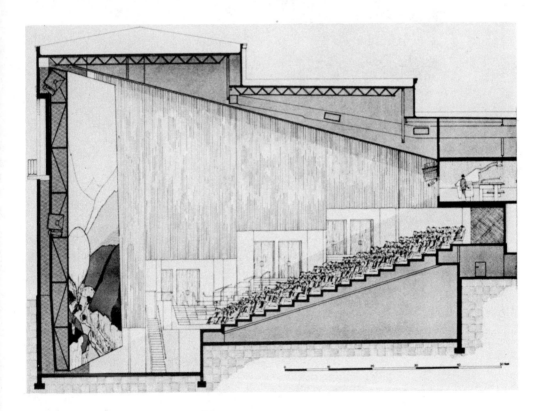

Figure 5-3. Typical IMAX theater. The effect of total immersion. (Illustration courtesy of IMAX Systems Corporation, Toronto, Canada.)

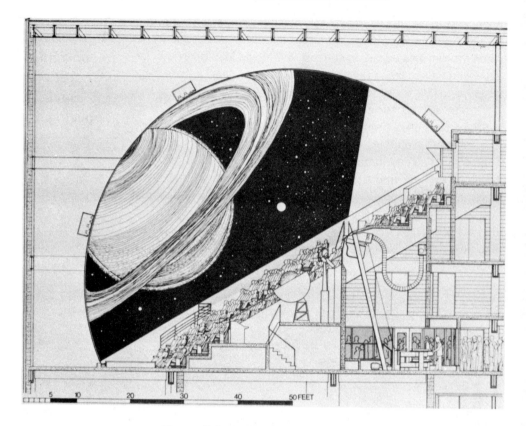

Figure 5-4. Typical OMNIMAX theater. (Illustration courtesy of IMAX Systems Corporation, Toronto, Canada.)

Supersize screens create the sense of "being there."

degrees above the horizon for centrally seated viewers. (See Figure 5-4.) In either case, the desired effect is one of "being there": The screen extends well into peripheral vision and requires eye/head movement to take in the entire image.

Having seen a short film on the history of flight in an IMAX theater, I can assure you that the effect of such immersion is very compelling indeed. You are totally enveloped by the image before you. Views such as that taken from a nose-mounted camera on a glider soaring over the rim of the Grand Canyon are heart-stopping.

THE USER AS ACTOR

Yet another sense of milieu is to be found within an interface that is measuring how your body is moving about. Consider the animation of humanlike figures on a TV screen by you yourself carrying out the movements you would like the figures to perform. This approach to human-figure animation, dubbed *scripting-by-enactment*, makes your programming of the desired actions literally a matter of showing the graphic figure what to do.[7]

Your actions become the script.

Light-emitting diodes are placed about your body (Figure 5-5). The diodes are sensed by a pair of special cameras as you move about. The two views of your actions, each from a different angle to provide stereoscopic vision, enable an associated computer to measure your actions three-dimensionally as you perform them. These recorded actions in turn become "scripts" for animation routines that map your just-completed actions to actions the graphic figure is to perform.[8] This figure may be a simple stick figure or a more substantial "cloud person" image (Figure 5-6). Later, in a separate graphic operation, the figures are clothed and fleshed out in whatever specific detail. Body type and the laws of physics are in principle alterable, as when the human scriptor is tall and thin but wants the final figure to be short and fat and walking about under lunar gravity.

After designating what one animated figure is to do by actually doing it, the user can go on to act out the part for a second character.

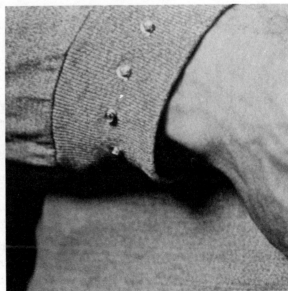

Figure 5-5. Human animation: light-emitting diodes plus a computer translate actions into illustrations.

75

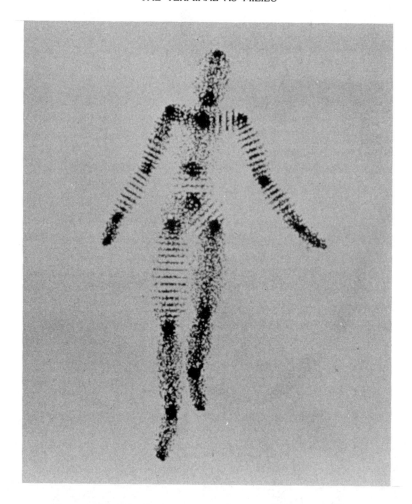

Figure 5-6. The "Cloud Person" figure driven by motions of the human scriptor. (Illustration courtesy of Delle Maxwell.)

Computer graphics can fill in the background and foreground.

This second character is scripted while watching, and interacting with, the first scripted figure as projected on perhaps a large Media Room screen. Environments and settings can be added in computer graphics to fill in background and foreground scenery. Such scripting-by-enactment in *context*—that is, in the midst of other characters and backgrounds—aids the human scriptor in tuning the movement of the current character to specific settings and events.

Such computer assistance is for the animator who wants to create characters-who-move but does not want to program (or per-

76

haps even to draw). Such a system might also help the playwright who prefers to act out creations rather than write them down. The computer-assisted dramatist could block out entire scenes, acting (and reciting) each part in turn. Upon playback of the completed scene, each voice part could be computer modulated to reflect the tonalities of the intended character. The dramatist, now turned director, "coaches" the characters by voice and gesture, perhaps further illustrating by movement how things are to happen.

NONPLANAR SCREENS

The screens we use at terminals need not always be flat and static. (I say "flat" though, strictly speaking, terminal CRT screens are typically slightly curved or spherical.) There may be circumstances where an "active" screen of a special shape is more in keeping with the information transmitted. An experimental instance of this innovative screen is the following excursion into "talking heads."[9]

Imagine, in the teleconferencing situation, that instead of conventional TV screens, translucent plastic masks are used as projection screens to show a speaker's face (Figure 5-7, see Color Insert). The mask is mounted on a pair of motor-driven swivel joints, permitting the mask to be tipped up and down and swung left and right. The speaker wears a lightweight position-sensing device—the space sensor described in Chapter 3—to capture head movement. The information from head movements is transmitted over telephone lines, multiplexed in with the speech signal. At the receiving end, the position information is extracted and used to animate the head.

Instead of a flat TV screen, imagine talking masks.

The facial image itself is not transmitted at all; it is stored locally on videodisk to be back-projected on the plastic-mask screen. The lips of the back-projected image are made to move in synchrony with the voice signal on the line. In our lab's experiments, we used both random bouncing of the lips (prerecorded lip movement, activated whenever voice is on the line) and speech-correlated lip movement, where the projected lip positions are selected in real time on the basis of nine broad phonemic classifications.

One aim of the experiment was to narrow the bandwidth required for teleconferencing by reducing that for transmitting the facial image to zero. Another was to enhance a sense of the "presence" of the person.[10] Yet another potential benefit was unanticipated when the experiments were made: The masks overcome executive reluc-

There's no need to compete with TV news correspondents.

tance to use teleconferencing at all. Much has been made of this drawback in users' acceptability of teleconferencing—the tendency to compare one's on-screen performance with that of network news anchors.[11] This tendency may arise in the first place precisely because one is using the same medium as the professional: a TV screen. Teleconferencing participants who instead sit in the midst of a set of virtual talking heads are not very apt, whatever their thoughts, to experience themselves and the other participants as being on TV. They may feel preposterous. But if they feel nervous, it's for reasons other than invidious self-comparisons to Dan Rather.

HIGHLIGHTS

- It's possible to penetrate solid space by means of half-silvered mirrors and a TV monitor. In fact, an observer can create three-dimensional images and manipulate them in space.
- Movie Maps—film footage transferred to videodisk plus supporting computer programs—can be used to create a milieu that combines the virtues of both overview and immersion.
- Scripting-by-enactment allows you to stipulate the actions of human figures on a TV screen without any knowledge of programming or even the ability to draw.
- TV screens need not always be flat. Translucent plastic masks, for example, can be used as projection screens to show a speaker's face.

NOTES

[1.] Gaston Bachelard, *The Poetics of Space*, translated from the French by Maria Jolas (Boston: Beacon Press, 1969).

[2.] Christopher Schmandt, "Spatial Input/Output Correspondence in a Stereoscopic Computer Graphic Work Station," *Computer Graphics* 17(3)(July 1983):253–261. The bibliography with Schmandt's article contains useful references to previous work on virtual-image graphic spaces.

[3.] See Schmandt, "Spatial Input/Output." See also John A. Roese and Lawrence E. McCleary, "Stereoscopic Computer Graphics Using PLZT Electro-Optic Ceramics," *Proceedings of the Society for Information Display* 19(2)(1978):69–73.

Polarizing glasses of the type used with commercial 3-D movies could of course also be used to create the stereo effect. There would then be a second TV monitor mounted at right angles to the first; the left and right halves of the stereo image would appear on either monitor. An additional half-silvered mirror mounted so that its plane bisected the angle between the two TVs would send the images from either TV along a common optical path, to the original half-silvered mirror, and thence to the observer. Transparent sheets of polarizing material would be placed directly in front of either monitor. The axes of polarization of these two sheets would be orthogonal to make the TV images separable by polarizing lenses mounted in eyeglass frames worn by the observer. The axes of polarization of these lenses would complement those of the polarizing sheets before the TVs to direct the filtered-out image from either monitor to the proper eye.

[4.] Are mental images "image-like"? There is currently in academic psychology a controversy whether mental imagery is analog in nature, or stored as propositions, or in both forms, or cast in yet some other format. The interested reader might consult Stephen M. Kosslyn, *Image and Mind* (Cambridge, Mass.: Harvard University Press, 1980), especially chap. 2, "The Debate About Imagery."

[5.] Andrew Lippman, "Movie-Maps: An Application of the Optical Videodisc to Computer Graphics," *Computer Graphics* 14(3)(1980):32–42.

[6.] William C. Shaw and J. Creighton Douglas, "IMAX and OMNI-MAX Theater Design," *SMPTE Journal* (Society of Motion Picture and Television Engineers) 92(3)(March 1983):284–290. IMAX and OMNIMAX are registered trademarks of IMAX Systems Corporation, 38 Isabella Street, Toronto, Ontario, Canada.

[7.] The scripting-by-enactment theme is from Richard A. Bolt, "Graphical Marionette," Funding Proposal, MIT Architecture Machine Group, 1981.

[8.] See Carol M. Ginsburg and Delle Maxwell, "Graphical Marionette," *Proceedings, SIGGART/SIGART Interdisciplinary Workshop on Motion: Representation and Perception* (New York: Association for Computing Machinery, 1983).

[9.] Nicholas Negroponte and William Parker, "Talking Heads: Display Techniques for Persona," paper presented at the Society for

Information Display International Seminar-Symposium-Exhibition, 27 April–1 May 1981, New York.

10. Nicholas Negroponte, Andrew Lippman, and Richard A. Bolt, "Transmission of Presence," Proposal to U.S. Defense Advanced Research Projects Agency (DARPA), Cybernetics Technology Division (Cambridge, Mass.: MIT Architecture Machine Group, 1980).

11. See "Firms Are Cool to Meeting by Television," *Wall Street Journal,* Tuesday, 26 July 1983, p. 35; Herb Brody, "Reach Out and Touch Someone," *High Technology* 3(8)(August 1983):53–59, especially p. 59.

6.

Future Interfaces

- *Circumstantial Indexing*
- *Multimodal Interaction*
- *Self-Disclosure*
- *Highlights*

A key assumption throughout this book has been that the person is the true terminal of any computer-based information system. That terminal is already designed. We can only design *for* it, incorporating human capabilities and limitations as explicit elements in our thinking about the total interface situation. In this final chapter, I identify three topics for further research that I feel are bound to influence future interfaces because they are profoundly rooted in how people relate to information. These topics are circumstantial indexing, multimodal interaction, and self-disclosure.

CIRCUMSTANTIAL INDEXING

Information retrieval strategies tend to focus upon the thing being retrieved as contrasted to the *circumstances* in which we last dealt with the item we want to get back. They stress the item, not your interaction with it.

Of course, much of what you might want to get from a data archive are things you've had no previous encounter with and can only describe in general terms—for example "all news stories about *Henry Kissinger* and *Nicaragua* dated between 7/1/83 and 8/16/83." Consider, however, those archived data items with which you, the user, have in fact had a prior encounter. Can your prior subjective experience with these items form a useful *coding dimension* for data retrieval?

Personal Memory Tags

Much, perhaps all, of what we remember of daily interpersonal transactions is "tagged" in memory with the time it occurred plus incidental particulars.[1] We naturally assume such memory encoding when, for example, in an office setting we might ask a co-worker:

"Hey—remember the blue economic report you showed me, oh, late last Friday, I think . . . ?"
"Sure . . ."

We tend to recall the *circumstances* surrounding such an event, even if the contents of the report in question were not all that memorable.

> *We tend to remember circumstances even when contents are forgotten.*

At the typical terminal, all transactions—invoices, mail, personal notes, whatever—occur in the *same spot*. A succession of things appear, each new item literally displacing the old. Further, on the majority of current terminals most messages look alike: lines of print. There is nothing distinctive about a message as it is embodied or presented that helps recall. There are just not enough distinguishing circumstances surrounding the message to make it memorable on any dimension *except* content. And if the message's content is not vivid or meaningful, then it tends to lose itself in the general stream of sameness.

Circumstantial Cues

Our memory mechanisms somehow let us easily recall where on a newspaper page a certain story was printed days, weeks, or even months after we read it.[2] These same talents for incidental memory for "place on the page" should also serve us well with a new kind of electronic newspaper. (Figure 6-1, *see* Color Insert.) Such a newspaper might begin to offer you retrieval of an article not only by subject, byline, and key words—that is, by content cues—but also on *circumstantial* cues: approximately which day you read the article, approximately what time, and, especially, where it was located on the page. Your request to the system would take the form:

> "Get me the article on 'personal computing' and 'banking'
> that I read . . . about three days ago, in the early after-
> noon . . . lower left column."

I am assuming natural speech input here—no mean trick—but what I want to focus on are the "circumstantial coordinates" of the request. The approximate *where* and *when* of your encounter with an article, coupled with denotation by key words, drastically narrow the bounds of search, and in many cases will uniquely define the target.

Imagine retrieving data by where and when.

Mutual Memories

In a data retrieval system that is sensitive to the personal aspects of your perusal of it, such incidental facts about your encounter with a particular item become, for *it* as well as for you, important retrieval dimensions. What the computer needs to do is keep a *complementary record* of its interactions with you. This record, like your memory, is indexed in part upon objective dimensions such as topic, byline, key words, and the like, and in part upon circumstantial dimensions: the "wheres" and "whens" surrounding your perusals. Later you should be able to say to the system:

> "Hey—remember the blue economic report you showed
> me, oh, late last Friday, I think . . ."

MULTIMODAL INTERACTION

Coordinated multimodal output in the direction from machine to person is not unprecedented. Motion pictures and television combine sight and sound. Video games do so emphatically. Certainly there have existed computer displays where something that blinked also buzzed. It is in the direction from person to machine that the current constriction—and future opportunity—lie.

Multimodal input is a future opportunity.

As I write this, there are personal computers coming on the market offering touch-screens and "mice" to enable manual input. There are also personal computers offering speech recognition options. What is yet missing is speech and manual input offered together in an *integrated* package. By integrated I mean not merely both available for use singly but available for use together in a coordinated manner.

Precise Wholes from Imperfect Parts

Not only can input from several sources result in a richer central impression, but high levels of efficiency and accuracy can arise from the convergence of two or more modes that themselves provide incomplete or imperfect information.

Nature has been quite inventive in this regard. For instance, snakes of two families—Crotalidae and Boidae, including rattlesnakes, water moccasins, and pythons—can integrate visible-light information coming through the eyes with infrared information coming in through special infrared "eyes" called pit organs—deep cavities in the head that open on the side of the head below and in front of the eyes. Warm-blooded (and hence edible) objects emit heat that is picked up by these infrared sensors and combined in the brain with the scene as rendered by the visual system to distinguish visible-and-warm objects in a unique "wide-spectrum" picture of the surrounding world.[3]

Two modes are better than one.

Computers, in certain areas, have been made to function in this spirit. "Researchers in computer vision recognize that imprecise information from many sources must be combined to understand the contents of an image."[4] So notes a recent journal article on machine interpretation of scenes: the extraction of spatial relations, the weighing of intensity values, the tentative identification of objects. The key word in that sentence is *imprecise*. Special approaches such as "fuzzy set theory" are invoked,[5] as well as deliberately teaching the machine to be cautious, to suspend judgment in the face of ambiguity, to await the development of additional information.

Redundant Modes

As implied by its name, the essence of the "Put-That-There" concept in Chapter 3 is the use of pronouns and pointing in lieu of designation through words only. Instead of having to say "the big green goblin with the yellow hair and the brown jacket" in order to specify him in a group of his cohorts, for example, you simply point and say "him." The direct benefits are twofold: less effort spent in generating verbal descriptions and less exposure to the vicissitudes of speech recognition.

Note that the information conveyed in either mode is not *redundant* with—that is, the equivalent of—that in the other. It is *supplementary*. Neither mode offers full information; they work in unison to form a complete meaning. In contrast, saying "the big green goblin" while in fact pointing at him would be a redundant use of modes. The speech part contains the *same* information, though in a different form, as the act of pointing.

Modes can be supplementary or redundant.

How might such redundancy work in a display situation reminiscent of "Put-That-There"? Let us assume that eyetracking has been added, so that three modes are present: speech, pointing, and eyes. Suppose, as in Figure 6-2, the user says "Move the triangle (looking at it) . . . there (pointing out where)." The user mumbles a bit on the word *triangle*. The eyes do light upon it, but only for an instant: something less than a strong fixation. Thus on either dimension—speech and eyes—the information that the system develops is less than definitive.

Now, if speech recognition alone were involved, the name of the item to be moved might be matched with such a low confidence rating that the system would decide to ask "What item?" But "triangle" is a reasonable though imperfect candidate for what was uttered; moreover, the eyes did indeed look at the triangle, however briefly. On the weight of the combined evidence, the system is willing to conclude that the user's intent is the triangle.

Evidence from redundant modes can converge on meaning.

The general procedure, then, is that when the speech part is ambiguous or uncertain, the system looks to information from eyes that may support whatever tentative decision was made on the basis of speech. The eyes are checked for possible confirmation of what happens in speech.

Certainly there is one situation in which we would not only seek supporting evidence in other modes but demand it: when we ask the system to do something that has irrevocable consequences. When I tell my word processor to delete a file, for example, I type in "D" and then the name of the file. The program doesn't delete it right away, but always asks me "Are you sure?" I must confirm by typing "Y" or "N." If you were using speech, hands, and eyes, the system might

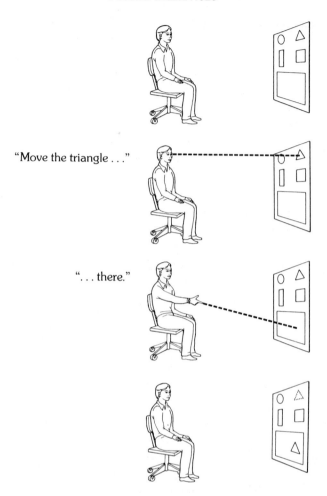

"Move the triangle . . ."

". . . there."

Figure 6-2. A multimodal command using speech, looking, and gesture.

well demand convergence in all three modes: While pressing the Delete button, you must also be looking at it and saying "Delete."

SELF-DISCLOSURE

Imagine: a computer-based body of information that unfolds itself to you automatically as a function of the curiosity and interest you show in it. This process of *self-disclosure* goes in both directions: The information base discloses itself to you as you disclose yourself to it.

What I have in mind is a system that not only responds to you on the basis of explicit inquiries via combinations of speech, touch, and gesture, but one that reacts automatically and subtly to cues and clues implicit in the way you look at it. Two kinds of knowledge would be vital to such a system: What is the user interested in? And how well is the user following the exposition of the topic?

Self-disclosure: mutual response to subtle clues.

We—or a computer system—cannot always know or anticipate beforehand what might be of interest to a person, or especially difficult, in any particular circumstance. And the ability of people to articulate their interests or puzzlements varies widely. In our special context—the human/machine interface—how might the system make reasonable inferences about what next to present and how to present it? With such highly graphic displays as those we have been considering—displays that are "out there" and visible—the strategy suggested is to *watch the eyes*.

Why Watch the Eyes?

One reason for the system to watch the eyes is to open a new channel through which we can detect where the user's attention is directed. The effect can be compared to what children gain when they discover that where the parent is *looking* is useful to them in comprehending what is transpiring between them and their parent, and, in turn, the world about them. "What has been mastered is a procedure for homing in on the attitudinal locus of another: Learning where to look in order to be tuned to another's attention. . . ."[6] That is how psychologist Jerome Bruner describes the significance of the child's discovery of the meaningfulness of the mother's line-of-regard when she looks at the cat and utters "kitty," looks at the door and utters "go out," and so forth. The significance of this event, translated to the human/machine sphere, is that awareness of the user's line-of-regard opens a subtle but powerful aspect of machine-to-human awareness.

Gaze reveals what is important.

There is yet another reason for the system to watch the user's eyes: The eyes *externalize* the focus of a person's attention and curiosity in a way that the ears, for example, do not. By watching people's eyes we know where their visual attention is directed. In contrast, we cannot tell *where* a person is listening; people's ears don't angle about like a rabbit's do. In fact, *eye direction may also be*

87

*Gaze is a good
index of
auditory
attention too.*

the best index of where auditory attention is directed. There is experimental evidence for a functional link between eye position and the
direction of auditory attention—namely, that we tend to listen in the
direction in which we are looking.[7]

What aspects of attention do eyes "externalize"? In the dynamic, multiwindow display situation described in Chapter 4, we
were concerned solely with which item (if any) the user is currently
looking at and how long the user has been looking at it. Now we are
concerned with the *overall pattern* of both eye movements and eye
fixations.

Types of Looking

*There are at
least three
kinds of
looking.*

Three types of eye movement have been distinguished by the
situations in which they occur.[8] The first is *spontaneous looking*. This
type of looking is governed by the novelty, complexity, incongruity
of visual stimuli. Such responses are "enduring dispositions," rooted
in the innate tendency to respond to contours and toward moving
objects.

The second type of looking is *task-relevant looking*. This is basi-
cally an allocation problem. The eye has sharp vision at its center, or
fovea, while peripheral vision is increasingly less distinct toward the
outer boundary (but very sensitive to movement). Thus sharp vision
occurs in sequential glances. The problem of where next to look is
resolved through the interaction of task constraints and the visual
environment.[9]

For an instance of spontaneous looking, note the patterns of eye
movements over faces shown in Figures 6-3 and 6-4. Looking concentrates where there is maximum figural information. For an instance of looking as a consequence of task requirements, examine
the eye-movement patterns shown in Figure 6-5. The first diagram
shows the result of free examination of the picture. Before each of
the subsequent recording sessions, however, the subject was asked
to estimate the material circumstances of the family in the picture
(diagram 2), give the ages of the people (diagram 3), surmise what
the family had been doing before the arrival of the "unexpected
visitor" (diagram 4), remember the clothes worn by the people (diagram 5), remember the position of the people and objects in the
room (diagram 6), and estimate how long the "unexpected visitor"
had been away from the family (diagram 7). While the image exam-

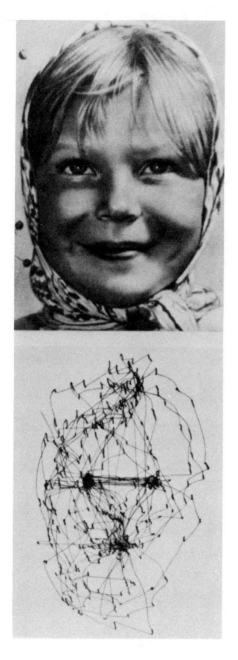

Figure 6-3. Record of eye movements during free examination of the photograph for three minutes. Here the looking concentrates where there is maximum figural information. (From Yarbus, 1967, used with permission.)

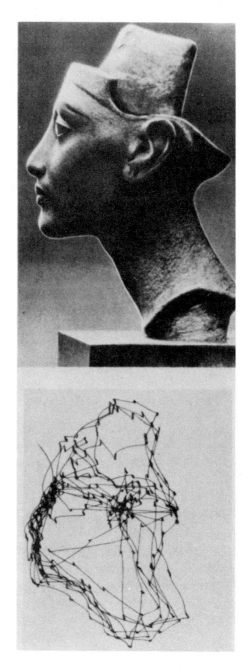

Figure 6-4. Spontaneous looking. Record of eye movements during free examination of the photograph for two minutes. Note the concentration of looking at the left-hand edge where informative detail of facial features is concentrated. (From Yarbus, 1967, used with permission.)

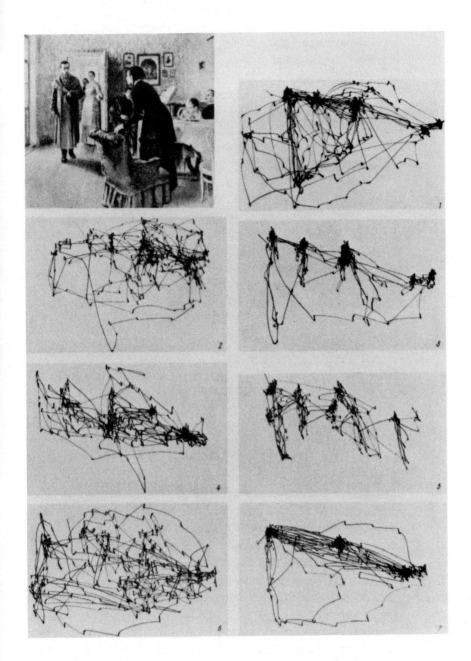

Figure 6-5. Task-oriented looking. Seven records of eye movements by the same observer, each record derived from three minutes of looking at the picture at the upper left. Here, however, the eyes are seeking answers. (From Yarbus, 1967, used with permission.)

91

ined remains the same, looking patterns vary as a function of the question the observer is trying to answer on the basis of scene content.[10]

The third variety of eye movements involves looking as a function of the *changing orientation of thought.* Movements of the eyes seem to reflect the overall transitions between states of thought, even when *where* the person is looking cannot possibly offer any new information (a sort of "gazing into space" phenomenon).

In general, then, where you are looking provides a ready index of what you are interested in (either for information or for pleasure), where you are going visually in order to gain information, and your overall cognitive set. There is a strong tendency to look where one thinks, even if the items of concern are no longer on view, as with jottings erased from a blackboard. Overall, patterns of eye movement and eye fixations have been found to be serviceable indicators of the distribution of visual attention as well as useful cues to cognitive processes.[11]

We tend to look where we think.

Pupil Size and Mental States

The time spent in looking at something can be taken as an ad hoc index of the amount of interest taken in it. Another indicator of interest is *pupil size,* a measure often provided by remote eyetracking apparatus. Pupil diameter has been related to the observer's level of attention and degree of effort.[12]

In particular, pupil diameter has been noted to increase upon viewing "pleasing" stimuli and to decrease when something "displeasing" appears.[13] Pupil size also appears to be related to the amount of ongoing mental activity. In a study of the interaction between pupil size and cognition, the pupils of the eyes of test subjects dilated when the subjects were presented with simple arithmetic problems. Size attained to a maximum when the solution was reached, decreasing immediately and returning to base level as soon as the answer was verbalized. If the subject was instructed not to recite the answer until told to do so, the pupils of the eyes remained abnormally large until the subject was asked for the solution; the size then decreased immediately. The increase in pupil size during the arithmetic task was proportional to the difficulty of the problem.[14]

Pupil size reveals effort and level of attention.

92

Orchestration of Presentation

Imagine that you are showing a guest, say it's your uncle, about your living room. You show him some animal miniatures arranged on the mantelpiece. As you comment, you notice that his eyes wander to the painting above the mantel. This movement becomes for you a cue to shift your commentary to the landscape that draws his eyes.

You may not be particularly conscious of your response. Indeed, to the extent that you are an accomplished host, it is more or less automatic. You are alert to what pleases your guest. With powers of observation like those of the skilled salesperson, you are keenly attuned to what he is saying, how he says it, all the subtleties of body language. Especially you rely upon where he is looking: the actions of the eyes.

We rely on the actions of others' eyes.

Then, after an anecdote about the picture, you notice that the sweep of your uncle's gaze is widening, taking in several other paintings as well. This suggests that he has attentively retreated from the single painting and is focusing now on the *group* of them. Your response is to widen your focus as well. You shift your commentary to a more general level and discuss the paintings as a group.

Perhaps some item on a nearby bookshelf then begins to catch your uncle's eye. Perceiving this, you start recounting how you came by it, what it means to you, and so forth. Or perhaps your uncle's eyes seem trained on no specific item at all. Your response then is to assume the initiative. You select the next item to be shown off. And so forth and so on. Throughout the visit, the eyes are a cueing mechanism between you and your guest. While I have emphasized the host's role, this cueing is two-way. As both of you talk, the topic, the pace, the ebb and flow of conversation are modulated by mutual eye interaction.[15]

Orchestration by Computer

Suppose we consider the orchestration of presentation again, but this time conducted by a computer-based information system. The equipment at the terminal should include color TV graphics, of course, touch and gesture sensing for manual input, and speech synthesis and recognition. The display screen might be of Media

Room scale, the eyetracking optics placed low at the screen's bottom edge. Or the terminal might be of the desktop variety. (See Figure 6-6)

Imagine a system that can tell what you want to see.

Suppose the system is showing you a historic house. It shows you an exterior facade view. While it narrates, your eyes move about over the picture. To enable you to speak to it, the system causes appropriate vocabulary items to be loaded into the speech recogniz-

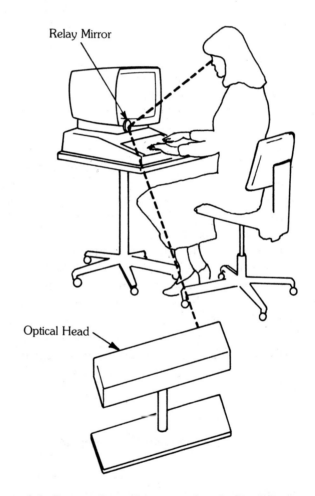

Relay Mirror

Optical Head

Figure 6-6. Eye-tracking the user of a desktop terminal is feasible with current technology. Eventually, tracking optics may be built into the terminal itself. (Schematic courtesy of G&W Applied Science Laboratories, Waltham, Massachusetts.)

94

er's store of active entries: words such as *roof, window, shutter,* and so forth.[16] Noting that you dwell on the Palladian window, the system zooms into that to show it off. It continues to comment about it—provided you still exhibit looking patterns that spell interest—in more detail than it normally would offer someone who hadn't been so intrigued. The system shows you the multiflued chimney in detail, too, because it finds from your looking patterns and pupil reactions that you continue to show special interest in it.

Inside the house now, the system at one point shows you, up close, a painting on the library wall. Your eyes sweep more broadly to take in paintings on either side as well. As a consequence, the view on the screen backs off a bit to include all three paintings. The narration generalizes to the *group* of them rather than any single one. Importantly, the system's speech recognizer, a moment before loaded with words specific to the one painting, now generalizes by bringing in vocabulary entries appropriate to general conversation about all three: a kind of verbal focus.

Voice and Gesture Too

Although I have been concentrating upon the eyes, speech and gesture play a role as well. At any time, the user can inquire about some item by pointing at it and asking a question about it. Further, the *scope* of your curiosity can be inferred from how your eyes are used, for example, in conjunction with speech.

Speech and gesture complement looking.

Suppose you utter "What's that?" as your eyes range broadly over a screen full of tiny images. Contrast that to your saying the identical words while gazing intently at some particular one of those little images. It is reasonable to infer that the scope of your curiosity is somewhat different in either instance. Accordingly, the system replies in the former instance "That's your old grammar school graduating class," while in the latter case it replies "That's you at age twelve."

Looking Away

You may well ask how, in a display driven primarily by eye, the system will know to zoom out after having zoomed in. That is, the system has zoomed you in on some item precisely because of the visual attention you paid it. If there is now no "elsewhere" on display to look, are you and the system somehow stuck there?

There are ways out. Perhaps *two* screens work in tandem. While screen A is holding a close-up of some one item, screen B offers a view centering on that item but including a wider perimeter about it. When you have perused the item on screen A to your satisfaction, to resume things you now look over to screen B. Screen A then switches to a wide view of what is on B. And so on and on. The general principle is that the "other" screen—the one not currently looked at—always holds a view of the material on the looked-at screen, but wider and more inclusive.

What if there's only one screen? In this case the system never zooms in too far on any item or area. Thus there's always enough "border" with things on it so that the user can look away.

Further—and this is a topic for specific research—the user's overall pattern of looking when surfeited may differ in reliable ways from the patterns produced when interested.[17] Detecting a shift to the former type of pattern would become a cue to begin to back off (zoom out).

Mutual Determination

Mutual interaction: both parties driving and driven.

Throughout, the user's experience and that of the system are mutually determined. The interchange at its best is not unlike one lively child showing another through a pile of favorite comic books. The motivation of one is to present; the other's desire is to browse. The imagery and narration presented by the system provoke the user's visual and voiced curiosity. The user's looking and asking determine what the system shows and says. The reactions and evocations are mutual: Either party by turn is both driving and being driven.

HIGHLIGHTS

- Since the mind tends to remember the circumstances surrounding an event, context constitutes a useful coding dimension. *Where* and *when* therefore become—along with byline, topic, and key words—useful coordinates in retrieving information.

- There is manual input (via the "mouse," for example) and there is vocal input (via the speech recognizer). What we need now is an integration of the two—or even three if we include eyetracking—to ensure that the system responds to our most subtle intentions.

- With suitable eyetracking technology, a system might anticipate our interests and intentions—through our pupil diameter and eye movements—and decide what graphic display we wish to see next. In such a system, speech and gesture too would play a role in sharpening focus.

NOTES

1. S. M. Smith, A. Glenberg, and R. A. Bjork, "Environmental Context and Human Memory," *Memory and Cognition* 6(1978):342–353.

2. E. B. Zechmeister and J. McKillip, "Recall of Place on the Page," *Journal of Educational Psychology* 63(1972):446–453.

3. E. A. Newman and P. H. Hartline, "The Infrared Vision of Snakes," *Scientific American* 246(3)(March 1982):116–127.

4. R. Jain and S. Haynes, "Imprecision in Computer Vision," *Computer* 15(8)(August 1982):39.

5. Brian R. Gaines, "Foundations of Fuzzy Reasoning," *International Journal of Man-Machine Studies* 6(8)(November 1976):623–668; cited in Jain and Haynes, "Imprecision."

6. Jerome S. Bruner, "From Communication to Language—A Psychological Perspective," *Cognition* 3(3)(1974–1975):269.

7. Daniel Reisberg, Roslyn Schreiber, and Linda Potemken, "Eye Position and the Control of Auditory Attention," *Journal of Experimental Psychology: Human Perception and Performance* 7(2)(1981):318–323.

8. From Daniel Kahneman, *Attention and Effort* (Englewood Cliffs, N.J.: Prentice-Hall, 1973), pp. 64–65. Kahneman notes: "The involvement of eye movements in mental processes attests to the linkage between the eye and the focus of attention. Thoughts often 'move' over a representation of space, and the position of the eyes tends to reflect the current direction of attention" (p.64).

9. See John W. Senders, "On the Distribution of Attention in a Dynamic Environment," *Acta Psychologica* 27(1967):349–354.

10. Alfred L. Yarbus, *Eye Movements and Vision,* translated by B. Haigh (New York: Plenum Press, 1967). The material in Figures 6-3, 6-4, and 6-5 is copyrighted by Plenum Publishing Corporation and reproduced with the permission of Plenum.

11. See Kahneman, *Attention and Effort,* pp. 60–61. See also M. A. Just and P. A. Carpenter "The Role of Eye-Fixation Research in Cognitive Psychology," *Behavior Research Methods and Instrumentation* 8(3)(1976):139–143.

12. Kahneman, *Attention and Effort,* pp. 18–27.

13. E. H. Hess, "Attitude and Pupil Size," *Scientific American* 212(1965):46–54.

14. Ibid. See also E. H. Hess and J. M. Polt, "Pupil Size in Relation to Mental Activity During Simple Problem-Solving," *Science* 143(1964):1190–1192.

15. M. Argyle and M. Cook, *Gaze and Mutual Gaze* (Cambridge: Cambridge University Press, 1975).

16. A special pool of global command words to control the automatic speech recognizer's general operation is of course always available in the recognizer's active vocabulary. "Pay attention" and "Stop listening" are examples. The words that are included beyond that are a function of context and circumstance. When used with our Dataland, for instance, the recognizer needs words for general navigational commands, such as "Go to the southwest corner" or "Go to calculator." Additional vocabulary entries are then item-specific words. When approaching the appointment calendar, for instance, words like "January, February, March . . ." are loaded in. Upon moving to the calculator, words such as "plus, minus, divide" are brought in, displacing (if necessary) word patterns for the calendar. This "verbal window" parallels in the speech realm the action of the worldview monitor's "you-are-here" marker in the graphic realm.

The term *verbal window,* along with the concept, is from Nicholas Negroponte (Architecture Machine Group memorandum, 2 July 1979). Making the speech recognizer's active vocabulary a function of where you are in graphic space is a more efficient use of the machine's finite memory space for vocabulary entries. The *effective* vocabulary of the recognizer expands from its momentary capacity of a hundred or so words to seemingly infinite size.

17. There is evidence, for example, that a person's looking patterns while trying to find a "hidden figure" in a presented scene differ

systematically from one's looking patterns after the figure has been discovered. See Lawrence Stark and Stephen R. Ellis, "Scanpaths Revisited: Cognitive Models and Direct Looking," in Dennis F. Fisher, Richard A. Monty, and John W. Senders (eds.), *Eye Movements: Cognition and Visual Perception* (Hillsdale, N.J.: Erlbaum Associates, 1981).

Bibliography

Allick, Jüri, Marika Rauk, and Aavo Luuk. "Control and Sense of Eye Movement Behind Closed Lids." *Perception* 10(1981):39–51.

Argyle, M., and M. Cook. *Gaze and Mutual Gaze.* Cambridge: Cambridge University Press, 1975.

Bachelard, Gaston. *The Poetics of Space.* Translated from the French by Maria Jolas. Boston: Beacon Press, 1969.

Bennett, John L. "Spatial Concepts as an Organizing Principle for Interactive Bibliographic Search." In Donald E. Walker (ed.), *Interactive Bibliographic Search: The User/Computer Interface.* Montvale, N.J.: AFIPS Press, 1971.

Bolt, Richard A. *Spatial Data-Management.* Cambridge, Mass.: MIT Architecture Machine Group, 1979.

Bolt, Richard A. "'Put-That-There': Voice and Gesture at the Graphics Interface." *Computer Graphics* 14(3)(1980):262–270.

Bolt, Richard A. "Gaze-Orchestrated Dynamic Windows." *Computer Graphics* 15(3)(1981):109–119.

Bolt, Richard A. "Graphical Marionette." Funding Proposal, MIT Architecture Machine Group, 1981.

Brody, Herb. "Reach Out and Touch Someone." *High Technology* 3(8)(1983):53–59.

Bruner, Jerome S. "From Communication to Language—A Psychological Perspective." *Cognition* 3(3)(1974–1975):255–287.

Bury, Kevin F., James M. Boyle, and Alan S. Neal. "Windows vs. Scrolling on a Visual Display Terminal." *Proceedings of the Conference on Human Factors in Computer Systems.* New York: Association for Computing Machinery, 1982.

Ciarcia, Steve. "Build the Micro D-Cam Solid State Video Camera." *BYTE* 8(9)(1983):20–31.

Cumming, G. D. "Eyemovements and Visual Perception." In E. C. Carterette and M. P. Friedman (eds.), *Handbook of Perception, vol. 9: Perceptual Processing.* New York: Academic Press, 1978.

"Dealing with Terminal Phobia." *Time,* 19 July 1982, p. 37.

DeBoor, C. *Applied Mathematical Sciences,* vol. 27: *A Practical Guide to Splines.* New York: Springer-Verlag, 1978.

Elphick, M. "Unravelling the Mysteries of Speech Recognition." *High Technology* 2(2)(1982):71–78.

"Firms Are Cool to Meeting by Television." *Wall Street Journal,* 26 July 1983, p. 35.

Flanagan, J. L. "Computers That Talk and Listen: Man-Machine Communication by Voice." *Proceedings of the IEEE* 64(4)(1976):405–415.

Foley, James D., and Andries Van Dam. *Fundamentals of Interactive Computer Graphics.* Reading, Mass.: Addison-Wesley, 1982.

Friedell, Mark, Jane Barnett, and David Kramlich. "Context-Sensitive, Graphic Presentation of Data." *Computer Graphics* 16(3)(1982):181–188.

Gaines, Brian R. "Foundation of Fuzzy Reasoning." *International Journal of Man-Machine Studies* 6(8)(1976):623–668.

"Get Vertigo Over Video Displays? Maybe It's a Case of Cyberphobia?" *Wall Street Journal,* 8 June 1982, p. 37.

Ginsburg, Carol M., and Delle Maxwell. "Graphical Marionette." *Proceedings, SIGGART/SIGART Interdisciplinary Workshop on Motion: Representation and Perception.* New York: Association for Computing Machinery, 1983.

Harris, Randall L., Sr., and David M. Christhilf. "What Do Pilots See in Displays?" *Proceedings of the Human Factors Society.* Santa Monica: Human Factors Society, 1980.

Hasher, Lynn, and R. T. Zacks. "Automatic and Effortful Processes in Memory." *Journal of Experimental Psychology: General* 108(1979):356–388.

Herot, Christopher F. "Spatial Management of Data." *ACM Transactions on Database Systems* 5(4)(1980):493–514.

Herot, Christopher F., and others. "Overview of the Spatial Data Management System." Technical Report CCA-81-08. Cambridge, Mass.: Computer Corporation of America, 1981.

Hess, E. H. "Attitude and Pupil Size." *Scientific American* 212(1965):46–54.

Hess, E. H., and J. M. Polt. "Pupil Size in Relation to Mental Activity During Simple Problem-Solving." *Science* 143(1964):1190–1192.

Hill, F. S., Jr., Sheldon Walker, Jr., and Fuwen Gao. "Interactive Image Query System Using Progressive Transmission." *Computer Graphics* 17(3)(1983):323–330.

Hochberg, Julian, and Virginia Brooks. "Film Cutting and Visual Momentum." In John W. Senders, Dennis F. Fisher, and Richard A. Monty (eds.), *Eye Movements and the Higher Psychological Processes.* Hillsdale, N.J.: Erlbaum Associates, 1978.

Hockett, C. F. "The Origins of Speech." *Scientific American* 203(3)(1960):89–96.

Hunter, M. L. *Memory.* Baltimore: Penguin Books, 1957.

Jain, R., and S. Haynes. "Imprecision in Computer Vision." *Computer* 15(8)(1982):39–48.

Just, M. A., and P. A. Carpenter. "The Role of Eye-Fixation Research in Cognitive Psychology." *Behavior Research Methods and Instrumentation* 8(3)(1976):139–143.

Kahneman, Daniel. *Attention and Effort.* Englewood Cliffs, N.J.: Prentice-Hall, 1973.

Knowlton, Ken. "Progressive Transmission of Grey-Scale and Binary Pictures by Simple, Efficient, and Loss-Less Encoding Schemes." *Proceedings of the IEEE* 68(7)(1980):885–896.

Kosslyn, Stephen M. *Image and Mind.* Cambridge, Mass.: Harvard University Press, 1980.

Lea, Wayne A. (ed.). *Recent Trends in Automatic Speech Recognition*. Englewood Cliffs, N.J.: Prentice-Hall, 1980.

Levinson, S. E., and M. Y. Liberman. "Speech Recognition by Computer." *Scientific American* 244(4)(1981):64–76.

Lippman, Andrew. "Movie-Maps: An Application of the Optical Videodisc to Computer Graphics." *Computer Graphics* 14(3)(1980):32–42.

Lopiccola, Phil. "Meet the Mouse." *Popular Computing* 2(5)(1983):102–105.

Lorayne, Harry, and Jerry Lucas. *The Memory Book*. New York: Ballantine Books, 1974.

McConkie, George W. "The Use of Eye-Movement Data in Determining the Perceptual Span in Reading." In Richard A. Monty and John W. Senders (eds.), *Eye Movements and Psychological Processes*. Hillsdale, N.J.: Erlbaum Associates, 1976.

Mandler, Jean, Dale Seegmiller, and Jeanne Day. "On the Coding of Spatial Information." *Memory and Cognition* 5(1)(1977):10–16.

Miller, George A. "Psychology and Information." *American Documentation* 19(3)(1968):286–289.

Miller, George A., G. A. Heise, and W. Lichten. "The Intelligibility of Speech as a Function of the Context of the Test Material." *Journal of Experimental Psychology* 41(1951):329–335.

Mintzberg, Henry. *The Nature of Managerial Work*. Theory of Management Policy Series. Englewood Cliffs, N.J.: Prentice-Hall, 1980.

Monty, Richard A., and John W. Senders (eds.). *Eye Movements and Psychological Processes*. Hillsdale, N.J.: Erlbaum Associates, 1976.

Morgan, Chris. "An Interview with Wayne Posing, Bruce Daniels, and Larry Tesler." *BYTE* 8(3)(1983):90–114.

Muter, Paul, Susane A. Latrémouille, and William C. Treurniet. "Extended Readings of Continuous Text on Television Screens." *Human Factors* 24(5)(1982):501–508.

Negroponte, Nicholas. "Soft Fonts." Paper presented at the Society for Information Display International Symposium, 28 April–2 May 1980, San Diego.

Negroponte, Nicholas. "Media Room." *Proceedings of the Society for Information Display* 22(2)(1981):109–113.

Negroponte, Nicholas, and Richard A. Bolt. "Augmentation of Human Resources in Command and Control Through Multiple Media Man-Machine Interaction." Proposal to U.S. Defense Advanced Research Projects Agency (DARPA), Office of Cybernetics Technology. Cambridge, Mass.: MIT Architecture Machine Group, 1976.

Negroponte, Nicholas, and William Parker. "Talking Heads: Display Techniques for Persona." Paper presented at the Society for Information Display International Seminar-Symposium-Exhibition, 27 April–1 May 1981, New York.

Negroponte, Nicholas, Andrew Lippman, and Richard A. Bolt. "Transmission of Presence." Proposal to U.S. Defense Advanced Research Projects Agency (DARPA), Cybernetics Technology Division. Cambridge, Mass.: MIT Architecture Machine Group, 1980.

Neisser, Ulrich. *Cognition and Reality*. San Francisco: Freeman, 1976.

Newman, E. A., and P. H. Hartline. "The Infrared Vision of Snakes." *Scientific American* 246(3)(1982):116–127.

Nievergelt, J., and J. Weydert. "Sites, Modes, and Trails: Telling the User of an Interactive System Where He Is, What He Can Do, and How to Get to Places." In Richard A. Guedj and others (eds.), *Methodology of Interaction*. New York: North-Holland, 1980.

Olson, D. R. "Language and Thought: Aspects of a Cognitive Theory of Semantics." *Psychological Review* 77(1970):257–273.

Pinxten, Rix, Ingrid van Dooren, and Frank Harvey. *Anthropology of Space*. Philadelphia: University of Pennsylvania Press, 1983.

Posner, Michael J., and Mary Jo Nissen. "Visual Dominance: An Information Processing Account of Its Origins and Significance." *Psychological Review* 83(2)(1976):157–171.

Rabb, F. H., and others. "Magnetic Position and Orientation Tracking System." *IEEE Transactions on Aerospace and Electronic Systems,* AES-15, no. 5, September 1979, pp. 709–718.

The Raster Graphics Handbook. Covina, Calif.: Conrac Corporation, 1980.

Rayner, Keith. "Eye Movements in Reading and Information Processing." *Psychological Bulletin* 85(1978):616–660.

Reddy, D. R. "Speech Recognition by Machine: A Review." *Proceedings of the IEEE* 64(4)(1976):501–531.

Reisberg, Daniel, Roslyn Schreiber, and Linda Potemken. "Eye Position and the Control of Auditory Attention." *Journal of Experimental Psychology: Human Perception and Performance* 7(2)(1981):318–323.

Rinard, G. A., and D. E. Rugg. "An Ocular Control Device for Use by the Severely Handicapped." Paper presented at the 3rd Conference on Systems and Devices for the Disabled, Boston, June 1976.

Rinard, G. A., and D. E. Rugg. "Current State of Development and Testing of an Ocular Control Device." Paper presented at the 4th Conference on Systems and Devices for the Disabled, Seattle, June 1977.

Robinson, A. L. "More People Are Talking to Computers as Speech Recognition Enters the Real World." *Science* 203(1979):634–638.

Roese, John A., and Lawrence E. McCleary. "Stereoscopic Computer Graphics Using PLZT Electro-Optic Ceramics." *Proceedings of the Society for Information Display* 19(2)(1978):69–73.

Schmandt, Christopher. "Soft Typography." *Information Processing '80.* New York: North-Holland, 1980.

Schmandt, Christopher. "Voice Interaction: Putting Intelligence into the Interface." *Proceedings of the Conference on Cybernetics and Society.* Los Alamitos, Calif.: IEEE, 1982.

Schmandt, Christopher. "Spatial Input/Output Correspondence in a Stereoscopic Computer Graphic Work Station." *Computer Graphics* 17(3)(1983):253–261.

Schmandt, Christopher. "Greyscale Fonts Designed from Video Analysis." *Proceedings, National Computer Graphics Association.* Fairfax, Va.: National Computer Graphics Association, 1983.

Schmandt, Christopher, and Eric Hulteen. "The Intelligent Voice-Interactive Interface." *Proceedings of the Conference on Human*

Factors in Computer Systems. New York: Association for Computing Machinery, 1982.

Schulman, Arthur I. "Recognition Memory and the Recall of Spatial Location." *Memory and Cognition* 1(3)(1973):256–260.

Schwarz, Elmer, Ion P. Beldie, and Seigmund Pastoor. "A Comparison of Paging and Scrolling for Changing Screen Contents by Inexperienced Users." *Human Factors* 25(3)(1983):279–282.

Senders, John W. "On the Distribution of Attention in a Dynamic Environment." *Acta Psychologica* 27(1967):349–354.

Senders, John W., Dennis F. Fisher, and Richard A. Monty (eds.). *Eye Movements and Higher Psychological Processes.* Hillsdale, N.J.: Erlbaum Associates, 1978.

Shaw, William C., and J. Creighton Douglas. "IMAX and OMNIMAX Theater Design." *SMPTE Journal* (Society of Motion Picture and Television Engineers) 92(3)(1983):284–290.

Smith, David Canfield, and others. "Designing the Star User Interface." *BYTE* 7(4)(1982):242–282.

Smith, Michael J., Barbara G. F. Cohen, and Lambert W. Stammerjohn, Jr. "An Investigation of Health Complaints and Job Stress in Video Display Viewing." *Human Factors* 23(4)(1981):387–400.

Smith, S. M., A. Glenberg, and R. A. Bjork. "Environmental Context and Human Memory." *Memory and Cognition* 6(1978):342–353.

Sondheimer, N. K. "Spatial Reference and Natural-Language Machine Control." *International Journal of Man-Machine Studies* 8(1976):329–336.

Stark, Lawrence, and Stephen R. Ellis. "Scanpaths Revisited: Cognitive Models and Direct Looking." In Dennis F. Fisher, Richard A. Monty, and John W. Senders (eds.), *Eye Movements: Cognition and Visual Perception.* Hillsdale, N.J.: Erlbaum Associates, 1981.

Steinman, R. "Role of Eyemovements in Maintaining a Phenomenally Clear and Stable World." In Richard A. Monty and John W. Senders (eds.), *Eye Movements and Psychological Processes.* Hillsdale, N.J.: Erlbaum Associates, 1976.

Stewart, George. "A First Look at Lisa." *Popular Computing* 2(5)(1983):84–92.

Tesler, Larry. "The Smalltalk Environment." *BYTE* 6(8)(1981):90–147.

Tullis, Thomas S. "An Evaluation of Alphanumeric, Graphic, and Color Information Displays." *Human Factors* 23(5)(1981):541–550.

Warnock, John E. "The Display of Characters Using Gray Level Sample Arrays." *Computer Graphics* (SIGGRAPH 1980 Proceedings) 14(3)(1980):302–307.

Williams, Gregg. "The Lisa Computer System." *BYTE* 8(2)(1983):33–50.

Winston, Patrick. "Learning Structural Descriptions from Examples." MIT Project MAC, TR-76, 1970.

Woods, David D. "Visual Momentum: A Concept to Improve the Cognitive Coupling of Person and Computer." *International Journal of Man-Machine Studies,* in press.

Yarbus, Alfred L. *Eye Movements and Vision.* Translated by B. Haigh. New York: Plenum Press, 1967.

Yates, F. A. *The Art of Memory.* Chicago: University of Chicago Press, 1966.

Young, Laurence R., and David Sheena. "Survey of Eyemovement Recording Methods." *Behavior Research Methods and Instrumentation* 7(5)(1975):397–429.

Zechmeister, E. B., and J. McKillip. "Recall of Place on the Page." *Journal of Educational Psychology* 63(1972):446–453.

Zinsser, William. *Writing with a Word Processor.* New York: Harper & Row, 1983.

Index

Allick, Jüri, 67n
animation, 74–77
Apple Lisa computer, 25–26
Applied Sciences Laboratories, 67n,
    68n
    eyetracker, 57–58
    extended head-tracking, 58–59
Architecture Machine Group, 5, 8, 60,
    70
Argyle, M., 98n
Aspen, Colorado, 72–73
Automatic speech recognition, 35–38
    coarticulation problem in, 38
    how done, 36
    kinds of, 37
    performance levels, 38
    progress in, 35

Bachelard, Gaston, 69, 78n
Barnett, Jane, 33
Beldie, Ion P., 31n
Bennett, John L., 32n, 33n
Bjork, R. A., 97n
Blood, E. B., 51n
body-tracking, 74–77
Bolt, Richard A., 7n, 30n, 51n, 68n,
    72, 73, 79n, 80n
Boyle, James M., 31n
Brooks, Virginia, 34n
Bruner, Jerome, S., 87, 97n
Bury, Kevin F., 31n

Carling, Richard, 33n
Carterette, E. C., 67n
Christhilf, David M., 66n
Ciarcia, Steve, 67n
circumstantial cues, 82–83
circumstantial indexing, 81–83
Cohen, Barbara G. F., 32n
computer-aided drama, 77
Computer Corporation of America
    (CCA), 21–25, 33n
connected speech recognition, 37
    in Media Room, 9
context in speech intelligibility, 39–40
Cook, M., 98n
Cooke, Alistair, 6n
Cumming, G. D., 67n
"cyberphobia," 2, 6n

Defense Advanced Projects Research
    Agency (DARPA), 5, 7n, 21
"Dataland," 9–20
    joystick travel in, 13
    locating data in, 12–13
    perusing data in, 13–21
    touch travel in, 13
    voice travel in, 13
    zooming-in on data in, 13–14, 19
Datalands,
    culture specific, 29
    personal vs shared, 27
    3-D, 29

data spaces, styles of
  infinite, 34n
  nested, 24–25, 28
  planar, 28
  windows in, 26, 28
data types in Dataland,
  books, 13
  calculator, 18
  film, 19
  letters, 16
  maps, 17
  telephone, 19
Day, Jeanne, 6n
DeBoor, C., 67n
Denver Research Institute, 67n
  eyetracking glasses, 55–57
Douglas, J. Creighton, 79n

Eames chair, in Media Room, 9
electronic shutter glasses
  see PLZT glasses
Elographics, Inc., 30
Ellis, Stephen R., 99n
Elphick, M., 50, n
eye as a pointer, 54
eyeglass-mounted tracking, 55–57
eyemovements, 53–54, 60, 62–63,
  87–96
  and changing orientation of thought,
    92
  looking "away," 95–96
  and speech recognizer vocabulary,
    94–95, 97n
eyes,
  externalization of attention by, 87–
    88
  as indicator of attitudinal locus, 87
eyetracking,
  acquisition of eye, 65
  calibration of tracker, 65
  ease of use, 64
  economics of, 64
  eyeglass-mounted, 55–57
  past uses of, 53
  remote, 57–59

filtering information by eye, 62
Fisher, Dennis F., 34n, 66n, 67n,
  99n
Flanagan, J. L., 51n

Foley, James D., 31n
Freud, Sigmund, 41
Friedell, Mark, 33n
Friedman, M. P., 67n
fuzzy set theory, 84, 97n

Gaines, Brian R., 97n
Gano, Steven, 68n
Gao, Fuwen, 68n
gaze-orchestrated "windows," 59–
  62
gesture,
  in conjunction with speech, 44–49
  when gesture is gesture, 41
Ginsburg, Carol M., 79n
Glenberg, A., 97n
Guedj, Richard A., 33n

half-silvered mirrors, 70
Hampton Court Maze, 71
Hartline, P. H., 97n
Harris, Sr., Randall L., 66n
Harvey, Frank, 34n
Hasher, Lynn, 7n
Haynes, S., 97n
head-tracking, 58–59
Heise, G. A., 50n
Herot, Christopher F., 33n
Hess, E. H., 98n
Hill, Jr., F. S., 68n
Hochberg, Julian, 34n
Hockett, C. F., 51n
Honeywell Occulometer, 67n
Hulteen, Eric, 51n, 52n
Hunter, M. L., 6n

I Incorporated, 30
IMAX motion picture system, 73–74,
  79n
intelligibility of speech,
  and context, 39–40
  to humans, 39
  to machines, 38–39

Jain, R., 97n
Jones, H. R., 51n
joysticks,
  in CCA system, 22

on Media Room chair, 9
use in Dataland, 12–13

Kahneman, Daniel, 97n, 98n
keyboards, 1–3
"keymaps," 13, 19, 21
Knowlton, Ken, 68n
Kosslyn, Stephen M., 79n
Kramlich, David, 33n

Latrémouille, Susane A., 32n
Lea, Wayne A., 50n
Levinson, S. E., 50n
Liberman, M. Y., 50n
Lichten, W., 50n
lip-movement, dubbing of, 77
Lippman, Andrew, 79n, 80n
Lopiccola, Phil, 34n
Lorayne, Harry, 7n
Lucas, Jerry, 7n
Luuk, Aavo, 67n

McCleary, Lawrence E., 78n
McConkie, George W., 66n
McKillip, J., 97n
managerial world, qualities of, 59–60
Mandler, Jean M., 6n
Maxwell, Delle, 79n
Media Room, 6, 8–9, 41, 42, 69, 71, 76
mental images, 79n
mental maps
  see spatiality
Method of Loci, 4
Miller, George A., 5, 7n 32n, 33n, 39, 50n
Mintzberg, Henry, 68n
MIT Architecture Machine Group,
  see Architecture Machine Group
Monty, Richard A., 34n, 66n, 67n, 99n
Morgan Chris, 34n
"mouse," 26, 84
Movie Map, 72–73
multi-modal interaction, 83–86
Muter, Paul, 32n

Neal, Alan S., 31n

Negroponte, Nicholas, 7n, 30n, 31n, 79n, 80n, 98n
Neisser, Ulric, 7n
Newman, E. A., 97n
Nievergelt, J., 32n, 33n
Nippon Electric Company (NEC),
  automatic speech recognizer, 41–42, 51n
Nissen, Mary Jo, 68n
nonplanar screens, 77

Olson, D. R., 52n
OMNIMAX motion picture system, 73–74, 79n
orchestration of presentation,
  by people, 93
  by computer, 93–95
overview vs immersion, 71–73

paging vs scrolling, 31n
Parker, William, 79n
Pastoor, Seigmund, 31n
percepts vs concepts, 71
personal "memory tags," 82
Pinxten, Rix, 34n
PLZT glasses, 70–71, 78–79n
PLZT electro-optics, 78–79n
pointing,
  "cone of indication," 41–42
polarizing glasses, 79n
Polhemus Navigation Sciences, Inc., 43, 51n
Polt, J. M., 98n
"ports," 22–23
Posner, Michael J., 68n
Potemken, Linda, 97n
"presence" in teleconferencing, 77
processing where looking, 62–63
progressive transmission of images, 62–64
pupil size
  as index of attention and effort, 92
  and mental activity, 92
"Put-That-There," 44–50, 71, 84, 85

Rabb, F. H., 51n
Rather, Dan, 78
Rauk, Marika, 67n
Rayner, Keith, 67n

Reddy, D. R., 50n
redundancy in modes, 84–86
Reisberg, Daniel, 97n
remote eyetracking, 57
Rinard, G. A., 66n, 67n
Robinson, A. L., 50n
Roese, John A., 78n
ROPAMS space-sensor,
  see space-sensing
Rosenberg, Ronni L., 33n
Rugg, D. E., 66n, 67n

Schmandt, Christopher, 31n, 51n, 52n,
  70, 71, 78n
Schreiber, Roslyn, 97n
Schulman, Arthur I., 6n
Schwarz, Elmar, 31n
screens,
  nonplanar, 77
  supersize, 73–74
  touch sensitive, 9, 72, 84
"scripting-by-enactment," 74–77, 79n
scrolling vs windowing, 31n
scrolling vs paging, 31n
Seegmiller, Dale, 6n
self-disclosing systems, 86–96
selective attention, 60
Senders, John W., 34n, 66n, 97n, 99n
Shaw, William C., 79n
Sheena, David, 67n
Simonides, 3–5
Smalltalk system, 25–26
Smith, David Canfield, 34n
Smith, Michael J., 32n
Smith, S. M., 97n
snake vision, as multi-modal, 84
"soft fonts," 31n
Sondheimer, N. K., 51n
space-sensing, 43–44, 71
spatial data-management system
  at CCA, 21–25
  at MIT, 5, 9–21
spatiality,
  mental maps, 3–5
  as mnemonic device, 3–5
  in task organization, 2–3
speech intelligibility,
  see intelligibility of speech
speech recognition
  see automatic speech recognition
speech recognizers, humans as, 39
Stammerjohn, Jr., Lambert W., 32n

Stark, Lawrence, 99n
Steiner, T. O., 51n
Steinman, R., 67n
stereoscopic vision, by computer, 75
Stewart, George, 34n
supersize screens, 73–74
synthesized speech, 18, 32n

"talking head" persona, 77–78
telebrowsing, 64
teleconferencing, 77–78
  executive avoidance of, 77–78
Tesler, Larry, 34n
3-D workspace, 72–73
touch sensitive screens, 72, 84
  in Media Room, 9
  use in Dataland, 13, 14, 18–21
touch travel
  in Dataland, 13
  in Movie Map, 72
touchpads,
  in Media Room chair, 9
  use of in Dataland, 15
Treumiet, William C., 32n
Tullis, Thomas S., 34n

USS Carl Vinson, 25

Van Dam, Andries, 31n
van Dooren, Ingrid, 34n
"verbal focus," 95
"verbal window," 98n
video text, extended reading of, 32n
videodisc, 19–20, 61–62, 72, 77
virtual image, 69–71
virtual stereoscopic images, 70–71
visual continuity, 27–28
voice travel, 13
Votrax Personal Speech System, 32n

Walker, Donald E., 33n
Walker, Jr., Sheldon, 68n
Warnock, John E., 31n
Weydert, J., 32n, 33n
Williams, Gregg, 34n
Winston, Patrick, 51n
windowing vs scrolling, 31n
Woods, David D., 34n
"World of Windows," 60–62

worldview monitor in Dataland, 11, 72
word reference patterns, 36–38

Xerox Star system, 25–26

Yarbus, Alfred L., 98n
Yates, F. A., 6n
"you-are-here" marker,
   in CCA system, 22

in Dataland, 12, 13
Young, Laurence R., 67n

Zacks, R. T., 7n
Zechmeister, E. B., 97n
Zinseer, William, 6n
"zooming-in,"
   by eye, 62
   by joystick, 22

ALSO AVAILABLE FROM LIFETIME LEARNING PUBLICATIONS:

MANAGING HIGH-TECHNOLOGY COMPANIES
By Henry E. Riggs (M.B.A.), Stanford University

This is the first book specifically addressed to the unique concerns faced by managers in high-technology business—emphasizing the daily operating decisions that ultimately determine the technology-based company's success. You'll gain practical insight into: managing and integrating the relationships between marketing, engineering, and production ■ identifying and capitalizing on new product opportunities ■ coping with pressure for growth ■ attracting, motivating, and managing creative professionals ■ analyzing different financial strategies ■ assuring product quality. 333 pages ■ 6½ x 9¼" ■ hardbound ■ $35.00

ERGONOMIC DESIGN FOR PEOPLE AT WORK, Volume 1
Workplace, Equipment, and Environmental Design and Information Transfer
by Eastman Kodak Company, Human Factors Section

This handbook provides practical guidelines for considering human factors in the design of equipment, environment, and workplaces in an industrial setting. Based on up-to-date research and over 20 years of experience and thought in ergonomics developed by Eastman Kodak's Human Factors Section of the Health, Safety and Human Factors Laboratory. Includes over 150 graphics and many tables, plus basic data on human capabilities. 406 pages ■ 6½ x 9¼" ■ hardbound ■ $45.00

DATA COMMUNICATIONS TECHNIQUES AND TECHNOLOGIES
by Joel Effron

This introductory guide presents a clear and easy-to-understand distillation of the vocabulary, techniques, and technologies of data communications. Designed for both novice and advanced communications professionals, it contains practical information and applications relating to micro, mini, and mainframe computers. Gives readers the understanding necessary for conversing intelligently with vendors and selecting appropriate hardware, software, and services. 225 pages ■ 6½ x 9¼" ■ hardbound ■ $29.00

WRITING HANDBOOK FOR COMPUTER PROFESSIONALS
by William D. Skees

A comprehensive writing manual designed exclusively for data processing and computer professionals. Includes techniques for writing effective correspondence, vendor surveys, systems analysis, design documents, and promotional presentations. Illustrated with examples from actual practice of good writing and helpful critiques of poor writing. Organized for quick, on-the-job reference by busy professionals. 296 pages ■ 6½ x 9¼" ■ hardbound ■ $27.50